151 Good Night Stories

MANOJ PUBLICATIONS

151 Good Night Stories

Publisher:

MANOJ PUBLICATIONS

761, Main Road, Burari, Delhi-110084

Mob.　:　09999476076, 9868112194,
　　　　　8178823569, 8178854810

Email　:　info@manojpublications.com

For online shopping visit our website : **www.manojpublications.com**

ISBN : 978-81-310-2241-2

CONTENTS

1. *Jim Loves Water Pistol*

Jim was the happiest child today. His father got him a water pistol. He imagined the fun he would have playing with his water pistol. Jim showed this wonderful toy to all his friends. His friends were equally excited. Jim told them that he would fill the pistol with water and shoot unsuspecting passers-by with it. 'I will enjoy and have fun!' Jim thought, 'I will drench everyone. People will run here and there.' Jim thought and laughed. Jim was so excited that he did not want to wait. He filled his water pistol with water and ran out to drench the first person he would see on the street. As Jim stood waiting for a passer-by, a car ran over a puddle. Splash! Poor Jim was drenched from head to toe in the muddy water. 'How bad!' Jim realised, 'I don't like to be drenched like this. No, I will never use my water pistol to drench others. They will feel bad.'

2. Pixie Carries away Berries

Poor little David was picking berries in the woods. Soon, David got tired. He lay down to sleep. David got up a little later. He was feeling refreshed. Suddenly, he saw the basket. "Oh! My God!" David wondered. The basket was empty. "Where have all my berries gone?" David was almost crying. But then, suddenly he saw a trail of berry pits and followed it. The trail brought David straight to a little pixie sitting under a tree, eating the berries. David became angry. "Why did you carry away my berries?" shouted David. "I found them under the bushes," the pixie answered. "No, they are mine. I can see a trail of pits from my basket to where you are sitting." David shouted louder. "I don't know these are your berries. I found them under the bushes in a basket. How do I know they are yours?" the pixie said, and she ran away laughing.

3. Sean and Brian Play Football

Sean had a new football. He was thrilled and excited as never before. His new football had the brightest red and blue with yellow stripes. No one had so colourful football as this one. 'Is it not the best football ever? I will not give it to any one, not

even to Brian,' he thought. In the evening, Sean went to the park to play with his new football. Suddenly, he saw Brian, his best friend, also coming to the park. Sean held the ball tightly looking the other side. 'Oh no! I will not share the football with Brian,' Sean thought sadly. "You have a beautiful football. Let us play together," Brian said smiling at Sean. "Yes," Sean said. Sean agreed to play with Brian. They began playing and laughing together. Sean enjoyed the game with Brian. He realised it is more fun when you share and play together.

4. The Garland of Flowers

Jasmine was dancing in joy as spring season was here. Jasmine loved flowers. She enjoyed playing with pink flowers. 'I will collect pink flowers. Pink is my favourite colour,' she thought. Jasmine went to the garden dancing in joy. In the garden, Aunt Marlene was weaving a garland of flowers. The blue, green, pink and yellow flowers in the garland were as colourful as a rainbow in the sky. Jasmine was very excited to see the flowers being woven in the garland. Jasmine wondered, 'How beautiful these flowers in different colours look!' "These flowers look so beautiful, Aunt Marlene!" Jasmine said with excitement. "Yes, my child! The garland looks beautiful because there are many flowers in it of different colours," Aunt Marlene said, "Each of us is as colourful and different as these flowers. Do you understand, my child?" "Yes aunt," Jasmine said. "So, we should praise and like everyone," Aunt Marlene said. Jasmine smiled happily.

5. Anthea Loves Monopoly Game

Anthea enjoyed the monopoly game. She enjoyed it even more when younger children lost to her. "It feels wonderful to buy an entire city or hotel," She would announce to younger children while playing with them. She enjoyed the game even

more while she played with her younger brother Jay. She always won the game and laughed when she made fun of Jay. Jay always lost the game. One day, Aunt Julia came to visit Anthea's family. She played the monopoly game with Anthea. Julia easily won the game as Anthea worked hard to win. But Anthea lost playing with Aunt Julia. When Anthea lost the game, she thought, 'Poor Jay! He must have worked hard while playing game with me. I should not have laughed at him for losing the game. I should behave kindly with him.' From that day on, Anthea never made fun of Jay when they played together.

6. *Jason Defeats the Evil Magician*

Jason, a brave young man, loved adventure. He was ready to help anyone. One day, he came to know about an evil magician. The evil magician had captured a young girl. Jason decided to save the girl. When Jason came near the evil magician's castle, he was horrified to see the young girl chained to the tower. "Don't worry! I have come to save you. I will defeat the evil magician," Jason reassured the girl. "I know. Please come near," said the girl, and she breathed fire! Jason quickly jumped and saved himself from burning. Jason realised that the magician had changed into a young girl. The evil magician could change into anything. Suddenly, the magician in the form of the young girl changed in his real form like the evil magician. He challenged Jason to fight. Jason fought bravely and defeated the magician. The magician ran away. Jason saved the girl and brought her back home.

7. **Sandra Makes the Snow Castle**

Sandra loved to make castles out of snow. Her mother often scolded her, "Sandra, you are so strange. Why do you waste your time playing in the snow? Why can't you make snow men like other children? Why do you make only castles?" Sandra never listened to her. She continued to make castles because she loved making castles. Once she was making a beautiful snow castle in the lawn. A lady crossing the street saw her making the castle. She came up to her. She was amazed to see the castles. "What's your name, little girl?" She asked. "Sandra," she replied. "Call your mother, Sandra," the lady said. Sandra called her mother. When Sandra's mother came out, the lady said, "I teach at a sculpting school. Sandra is very talented. Please, you must send her to participate in our sculpting contest!" Sandra participated in the contest. She won the contest.

8. The Harp Brings Happiness

Once upon a time, there was a happy kingdom. In this kingdom, there was a magical harp. Its music spread happiness and joy everywhere. One day, the harp disappeared. "Where is the harp? Where is the harp?" everyone asked. No one had the answer. Then a brave knight went to see the wise old man of the mountains to find the harp. The old man said, "The harp has gone away because it is sad. The harp is sad because the kingdom does not care about it anymore. If you play happy music, the harp will be pleased to come out of its cave." When the knight played the happy music with his flute, the harp came out of the cave. The people of the kingdom said, "We love you, dear harp. Don't leave us ever again." The harp promised never to leave, if people loved it. Once again, happiness returned to that land.

9. Emma Loves Nature

Emma was very nervous. She had never been to school but now she will have to go to a school. Her parents were moving to a new town to settle there. The mother

said, "Emma, our dear child! You will now go to a school. Be ready for the admission test." "Mom! How will I take the test? I don't know anything." Her mother said, "Don't worry, my child! Most children learn by reading about things in books. But you have seen and observed those things while playing in the woods. You have seen them in Nature." The exam results came. Emma had scored full marks. The teacher asked, "Emma, who taught you all these things?" Emma said, "My grandparents took me on fishing trips, jungle walks and bird watching. I saw how plants grew, watched the birds fly and thunder spark across the sky. Nature has taught me everything."

10. Home Work on Kindness

Samuel's class teacher announced in the class, "Children, you have to write on one act of kindness you have done. This is your project for which you will be awarded grades. Go and do your best." Poor little Samuel did not know what to do. 'What shall I write about? I don't know anything,' Samuel thought. Some of his friends were visiting an orphanage, while others were going to visit slums. "Mom, what shall I write in my project?" he asked his mother. His mother said, "Samuel, you know what you have to do." "What mom?" Samuel asked. "Don't you ask me to pack some slices of bread in your lunch-box to feed the homeless puppies? This is kindness. You already know about kindness because you act like a kind person. You are kind at heart. Just write about it," the mom said. Samuel wrote about feeding the puppies. He got 'A', the best grade.

11. The Friendly Gnome

When Jane's mother placed a garden gnome near the row of daisies in the garden, Jane did not feel comfortable. "Mom, won't the poor gnome feel hot standing out there all day in the sun?" she asked her mom. Jane's mother didn't reply. So, she took her own umbrella and covered the gnome with it. Jane was happy to shelter the gnome. A few days later, it rained heavily one day. The ground became slippery. Jane slipped on the ground. She scraped her knee and twisted her ankle. She would have to stay home for a few days. She was crying helplessly. She thought how happy she was before the pain. When she woke up the next morning, she was feeling miraculously better! There was a note on the windowsill: "One good turn deserves another. Thanks for the umbrella." The garden gnome had used his magic to cure her!

12. *Listen to Elders*

Amy and her grandmother lived together in a cottage. Their cottage was at the edge of the forest. She would go alone in the forest, while her grandma felt worried for her. One day, her grandma told her, "Amy, remember; never visit the old castle at the heart of the forest. It is not safe for you, my dear child." Amy agreed, but she did not pay attention to grandma's warning. One day, she ignored grandma's warning and went alone to see the castle. When she reached the middle of the forest, she found the castle just in front of her. "Oh, this castle is so ordinary," Amy said. Suddenly, the rose vines in the garden started to grow and stretch towards Amy. A vine

wrapped itself around her ankle. Amy immediately ripped it off and ran from there. Amy would always listen to her grandma and elders from that day on.

13. *Make Your Palace of Truth*

Fairy Godmother cared for little children on earth. She called all fairies and sprites one day to announce her plan. "We will soon build two palaces–a palace of truth and a palace of lies," Fairy Godmother said. "Why will we build two palaces?" the fairies

and the sprites asked. "Because every time a child speaks the truth, a brick is created and the fairies will build the palace of truth. In the same way, a brick is created when a child tells a lie and the sprites will build the palace of lies. Have you followed?" Fairy Godmother asked. "Yes, Fairy Godmother," they said in unison. The good fairies went all across the earth. They taught children how to speak the truth. Soon, the palace of truth was built. All children can help the fairies to build the palace of truth, if they always speak the truth!

14. *Melissa Helps the Water Fairy*

One day, Melissa was playing at the beach. Just then, she heard a voice. Melissa listened carefully; someone was calling for help, "Help me, get back to the sea!" Melissa looked towards the direction the voice was coming from. She saw a tiny lady inside a seashell. 'A water fairy in distress!' thought Melissa. She helped the water fairy out of the shell and carefully placed her in the water. A few days later, Melissa visited the beach again hoping to find the water fairy. The weather turned rough suddenly. Huge waves crashed down on the sand. Melissa became worried. As soon as Melissa turned to leave the beach, a huge wave swept across her. She was suddenly dragged down into the sea. Melissa started drowning. She cried for help. Suddenly, she felt someone pulled her to safety. She saw the same water fairy save her in return.

15. *The Magical Stone Basin*

One day, Daniel found a carved, stone basin. Daniel wondered what the use of this stone basin was. He poured some water into it. Lo and behold! Daniel saw images forming on the surface of the water in the basin. Daniel wondered as he saw film-like moving images forming over the surface of the water in the basin. He was amazed to see scenes from all over the world. "How wonderful!" Daniel wondered. The images disappeared suddenly. The images formed again, when Daniel looked away. Daniel consulted a wise man to learn about the magical basin in which images appeared and disappeared. The wise man said, "The basin shows the future. But sometimes, God does not want us to know today what will happen tomorrow. So, the images disappear before you can understand them!" Daniel gave the basin to the wise man. He never looked at the basin again.

16. Andrew and the Magic Rocket

Andrew loved toys. He liked all kinds of toys but he liked guns and rockets more than any other toys. His father and uncle always gave Andrew new toys to play with. One day, his uncle Joseph gave him a rocket that looked like a real rocket. Andrew loved the new rocket because he thought it could fly. "Wow! My rocket will go straight into the sky," Andrew shouted in joy as he imagined his rocket flying up in air. While he was playing with the toy, his younger cousin, David, came there. "Look David! Here's my new rocket," Andrew said showing

his rocket to David. "And now, this magical rocket will fly in the air," Andrew thought that he would fool David. "Really! Show me the flying rocket," David said. When Andrew released the rocket into the air, the rocket fell down. "The battery of the rocket is not working," David smiled. Andrew understood he could not fool David.

17. The Tunnel with Gifts

One day, Randy was going alone through a dense forest. Then he noticed a big tunnel in front of him. "Oh My God! This tunnel is so long," Randy said. The surprise

didn't end there. There were more surprises waiting for Randy as he entered into the tunnel. There was a table in the tunnel with lots of fruits and delicious food. Randy tried to pick an apple up but the table disappeared. He was disappointed but he moved on. He saw a shelf full of toys at the next turn. When Randy tried to pick some toys up, they vanished. Randy next saw a box full of chocolates. Randy did not touch the chocolates. 'I don't want anything, if it disappears,' he thought. After long, he arrived at the end of the tunnel. Wow! There was a box of chocolates but he had not touched! He was rewarded because he stopped being greedy.

18. The Reward of Hard Work

There was a barren piece of land outside the village. No plants grew there. Everybody said that nothing could ever grow there. Then one day, a hard-working man came and built a small hut there. He lived with his two sons and a daughter. The next day, he began tilling the land. He worked very hard. His two sons and daughter also helped him. The neighbours laughed at him. They said he was working on the land where nothing could grow. Several months passed as the man continued working hard. The land which was barren once now had crops growing. Those who laughed at him were surprised to see that he had the best crops in the village. Soon, the man built a neat little cottage. Some more years later, the cottage became a two-storey house. The villagers realised that hard work can turn a barren land to a fertile one.

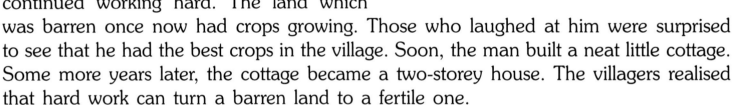

19. God Answers Prayers

On Saturday, there was a Christmas party at school. Poor Penelope did not have a nice dress to wear. Her mother did not have enough money to buy her a new dress. Penelope became sad. Then she thought, 'God helps…sincerely.' Penelope prayed to God. "Dear God! I will be a good girl to my mom. I will help my mom and I will never trouble her. Dear Holy Father! I want a new dress for the Christmas party at school." "Amen!" Penelope thought that she clearly heard God's voice. It was Saturday morning. Penelope still did not have the new dress. The party was about to start in a few hours. Suddenly, she saw her mother come rushing into the house. She brought a pretty golden frock. "I got Christmas bonus, so here is a new dress for you," the mother said. Penelope understood God had answered her prayers.

20. *The Secret Hollow*

Gemma, Georgia and Ginny were happy that day. They were visiting their grandparents. 'How wonderful is grandfather's garden? We will have real fun there,' they thought. The children never tired of running around their grandparents' garden. There was an old but huge oak tree in a corner of the garden. "Look at this huge tree! We can have real good time here!" exclaimed Gemma. The other children came running to see the big tree. The tree had a huge hollow large enough for a child to enter. Ginny was the first to crawl in. She found the hollow trunk was as large as a little room. "Gemma, Georgia, where are you? Come; hurry up," she called. The girls too entered inside. The children began to have parties inside the hollow every day. Their grandparents wondered what made the children so excited in the garden. But it was their little secret that they did not disclose.

21. *The Animal World*

In a toy store, the little toys came to life at night. The little toy cat was arrogant. She laughed at the other toys. "I am much prettier than all of you. You all are so ugly," she said proudly. The toy bear went to her and said, "Will you play with me?" "No. You look so ugly. How can I play with you?" the toy cat mewed. The bear walked off sadly. The cat had no manners. She did not know how to speak politely. A toy dog came there next day. The dog did not like the bad manners of the cat. He jumped at her to bite off her tail. Suddenly, the bear came to save the cat. The toy dog ran away. "I am sorry for treating you badly," the cat said to the bear. From that day on, the cat was nice with every animal. They all became friends.

22. The Foolish Hyena

A hyena stole a calf one day from a farm near by. The hyena wanted to eat up the calf quietly in its lair. Once they were in the lair; the calf felt nervous and fearful. But the calf was intelligent and thought of a scheme to save its life. "I am told that you have a unique laugh. All the animals in the forest tremble in fear when you laugh. Please let me hear you laugh before I die," the calf spoke fearfully. The foolish hyena felt flattered. He said, "You must be an intelligent calf to have heard about my qualities. I will certainly fulfil your wish!" So, the hyena started laughing loudly. His laughter was cruel and menacing. The farmer was alarmed when he heard the loud laugh. He realised that a hyena had stolen his calf. He followed the sound and immediately killed the foolish hyena!

23. The Flower Fairy

One day, Janice wondered at all the petals that dropped down from flowers every day. So, she asked the friendly gardener, "What happens to all the petals that drop down from flowers each day?" "The wind blows them away, my sweet child!" the gardener replied. Next evening, Janice sat looking at the flowers in the garden out of her window. Suddenly, the wind began blowing. The whirl wind grew stronger. The strong wind carried all the petals in its swirling motion. The petals started flowing in the air. She ran out to see the petals swept away by wind. There, stood a beautiful lady over the heap of petals. "Who are you?" Janice asked. "I'm a flower fairy. I take the colours from the fallen petals to fill colours in this world," she said. From then on, Janice was always reminded of the flower fairy whenever she saw a fallen petal.

24. Never Give up

Colossus was a king. His enemies were hounding him. Once, Colossus went to hide in a cave to escape from his enemies. Although he was a king, yet he had to hide from his enemies. 'Now I am in a safe place,' Colossus thought. Colossus was pondering over his next move while in the cave. Suddenly, he saw a spider. The spider was weaving its web at the mouth of the cave. It was working non-stop going from one end to the other. It fell several times but got up each time. It never gave up. The spider continued weaving its web on and on without bothering for the world. Finally, it made its web. Watching the spider, Colossus learnt never to give up. No task is impossible, if you don't give up. Colossus now went to the battlefield. He fought against his enemies bravely. Finally, he won his kingdom back.

25. The Maple Tree

Once, there were many tall trees in the forest. But there was a small maple tree among all the tall trees. The maple tree always felt he was unlucky. He thought, 'I am so small that no one cares for me.' The birds made their nest on nearby trees, but not on the maple tree. The maple tree felt sad and complained that the birds did not like him because his branches were small. He felt jealous of the tall trees when they swayed and danced with the wind. The wise old peepal tree explained to him, "Dear maple! Count your blessings, my son. It's not a curse to be small!" One day, a man with a machine came and started cutting the big strong trees. But the maple tree was left because he was not tall. That day onwards, the maple thanked his creator for making him small.

26. The Jealous Cloud

There was a cloud named Silver-rain. She lived over a beautiful kingdom. She blessed the kingdom with rainfall and made the kingdom green and prosperous. Although Silver-rain was herself big yet she saw a bigger cloud one day. Silver-rain felt jealous of the bigger cloud. Jealousy is never good. Silver-rain did not know that jealousy would harm her. "I'll keep all my water and never rain again, till I am as big as that cloud," she decided. Soon, Silver-rain grew bigger because she did not rain. But the kingdom suffered a drought because there was no rain. Silver-rain grew bigger and bigger. But she did not grow bigger after sometime because there was no water for her to grow. Now she began to grow smaller and smaller. Her selfishness created this problem. She began to cry. Her tears were rainfall. The drought was over! Silver-rain never became selfish again.

27. The Proud Lion

Once upon a time, there lived a proud lion in the jungle. He hated other animals and made fun of them. An elephant also lived in the same jungle. The lion laughed at the elephant and called him clumsy. One day, the lion called all the animals in his den for a meeting. The animals assembled in the lion's den out of fear. However, the elephant did not come, because the lion had called him clumsy. He did not fear the lion. Suddenly, a landslide sealed up the den when the animals were inside. So, a bee flew out through a tiny gap between the rocks to seek the help of the elephant. The elephant moved the rocks. The animals were saved. The lion was sorry for his past behaviour. He said, "I have learnt my lesson. From now on, I will never make fun of anyone."

28. James Learns a Lesson

Little James was fond of his toys. He loved to play with his toys, but he always went to bed without tidying up his room. His room always looked much untidy. No one likes an untidy room. James' toys especially hated his untidy room. So, they began complaining to James. One morning James was shocked when a teddy bear jumped up and said, "James, how can I play with you? Your room is so untidy," James became sad. Next, an old wooden soldier complained, "James, why do you always leave us untidily on the floor? You don't know how uncomfortable and cold the floor is!" James remembered how comfortable he felt in his bed. But he had felt bad when he had once slept on a chair. James asked them to forgive him. Now he always put his toys nicely in their places before he went to bed.

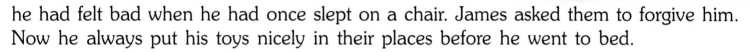

29. The Lesson for Elves

Once, a group of elves and dwarfs lived together with Fairy Godmother. The elves always made fun of an old dwarf. Fairy Godmother did not like the behaviour of the elves. She decided to teach the elves a lesson and cast a spell on them. The spell was effective. After the spell had become effective, whatever the elves said its opposite happened to the old dwarf but the same thing happened to the elves. Next time when the elves called the dwarf 'an old fool', he became younger and more intelligent, but the elves became older and also foolish. "Why are we becoming old and foolish?" the elves wondered. None had the answer except the Fairy Godmother. Fairy Godmother said, "I have put a spell on you, so you understand how cruel you were behaving." The elves said they were sorry and felt ashamed of their behaviour. Fairy Godmother then turned them back into their true forms.

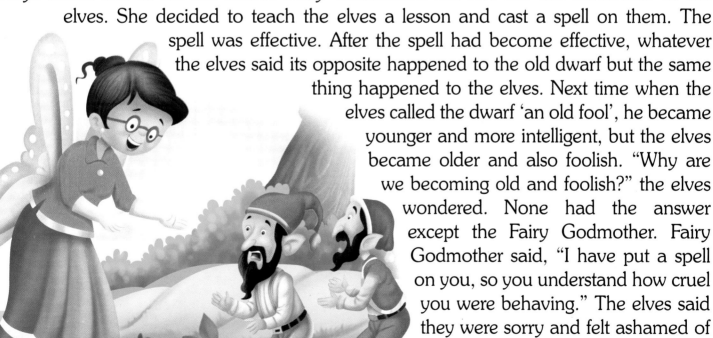

30. Win Hearts

Anna and Annabelle loved sports. They did not miss any sporting event opportunity in the school. They were training for a running competition in school. They practised every day for many months. Anna and Annabelle were competitors because they were participating in the same event. Competitors are not enemies. They should interact and speak to one another. Though Anna and Annabelle practised together yet they never spoke to each other. On the day of the race, Anna ran well, and won the race. Anna was happy but Annabelle was unhappy. Annabelle was disappointed at not having won, but she went to congratulate Anna on her win. Anna was surprised and impressed with Annabelle. She had never seen anyone who had lost the race behave so sportingly. Anna said, "Thank you, Annabelle. We may win and lose many races, but with your sporting spirit you will always win hearts and make friends."

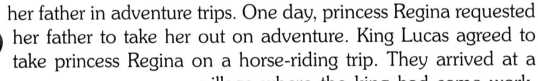

31. Regina Stopped Lying

Princess Regina, daughter of King Lucas, was spoilt. She did not listen to the advice of elders. She often told lies. She loved adventure and accompanied her father in adventure trips. One day, princess Regina requested her father to take her out on adventure. King Lucas agreed to take princess Regina on a horse-riding trip. They arrived at a village where the king had some work. In the meantime, Regina started troubling everyone. Suddenly, the king found Regina playing pranks. She lied, "Father, there is a girl here who looks just like me. She did all these bad things." But the king knew the truth. He came to the palace, leaving Regina behind in the village. Regina was sorry that she did not behave well. She stopped lying and behaved well. When the king saw that she had changed, he forgave her and took her back home.

32. The Dog and the Rabbit

Once there was a farmer who had a dog and a rabbit. He wanted to test the skill of his pets. So, he hid a carrot and a bone in a hole in his field. He then held a competition between his dog and the rabbit to see which animal would find them first. The rabbit always thought he could do any job. The optimistic rabbit dug here and there, convinced that he would

find the carrot. But the dog did not have self-confidence. He thought he could not do any job well. After sniffing around for a while, the pessimistic dog sat on the ground and complained, "It's too difficult to find a bone in such a big field!" The rabbit finally dug a tunnel right under the dog. There, he found the carrot and the bone. The dog lost because of his pessimism although the bone was right there.

33. The Importance of Sharing

Tim and Joe were good friends and always played together. They also quarrelled sometimes. However, they never shared their food. One day, they were playing under the apple tree. There was just one apple left on the apple tree. They both saw the apple at the same time and ran to pluck it. When they reached the tree, they started arguing as who should pluck and eat it. "I will have this apple," Tim said. "No, I will have this apple," Joe shouted back. The gardener working near by thought the boys did not know how to share. He decided to teach them a lesson. He went, plucked the apple and said to them, "See, this is what happens when we fight! I got the apple instead of you! If both of you had decided to share it, you would be enjoying this juicy apple instead of me!" Tim and Joe learnt the importance of sharing.

34. *Jude Found a Magnifying Glass*

Jude loved to tinker with gadgets. One day, he found an old magnifying glass in the attic of his house. Jude held the glass in his hand and looked at it over and over again. He was curious about the glass. He used the glass to look at an ant. "Wow! The ant has become so big," exclaimed Jude as he looked at the ant through the glass. But when he took the magnifying glass away, the ant stayed the same size. "This is the magical glass!" remarked Jude in surprise. He ran to his mother and said, "Mother, look! I have found a magical glass. If I place something under it, that thing grows big in size. I will use it on my sweets and chocolates!" His mother said, "Jude, this is a magnifying glass, which only makes things look bigger. They actually remain the same size!" Jude was very surprised indeed!

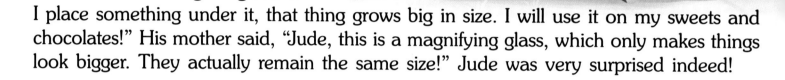

35. *Maria Loves Birds*

Maria loved birds. She was excited to see the birds of different colours in the garden. She would be thrilled to see them fly in the air. Maria was visiting her Aunt Jennifer. She was excited about the visit because Aunt Jennifer had seven parakeets. All the

seven parakeets were of different colours. Maria thought it would be wonderful to see the beautiful parakeets and play with them. Maria felt sorry for the birds seeing them caged. The birds were sad. They were not singing or chirping. But the free grey sparrow outside the window was chirping to greet the sunny day. "Why must the birds be caged all the time?" Maria asked. "Well, they will fly away if they are not caged," said her Aunt Jennifer. Maria said, "But if God does not cage us, why do we cage the birds?" "Maria, you are right," Aunt Jennifer realised. She released the parakeets into the sky.

36. The Statue of Lion

Jack and Jim were friends. They played together and cared for each other. There was a park near Jack's house. In the centre of the park, there was the statue of a lion carved in stone. The statue looked so real as if it was about to spring to life. Jack and Jim always looked at the statue in awe. Jim often joked that the stone lion would surely jump off the pedestal one day. One afternoon in the park, both boys ran to the statue only to see an empty pedestal. The stone lion was now standing on the ground. "Look Jack; I was right! The stone lion jumped off the pedestal!" Jim was brimming with excitement. The gardener near by heard him and said, "Oh no, the pedestal is being repaired. That's why we moved the lion!" The boys laughed and went to play.

37. Power of Prayer

Simon was a naughty boy. He hated sermons and didn't like to pray. He often laughed during the priest's sermon. 'Prayer is a waste of time!' Simon would think. "I should be playing right now. I don't want to listen to silly sermons," he often complained to the grandmother. One day, Simon's grandmother fell ill. Simon became very worried for his grandmother. He did not know what to do. Then he was reminded of the priest. So, he went to the priest and asked him for help. The priest reassured Simon. He said, "Simon, prayer has the power to heal. If you pray from the heart for your grandmother, she may recover soon." Simon, worried about his grandmother, began to pray at once. He was now at peace with himself. To his relief, his grandmother also started recovering. Simon never laughed at the power of prayer again.

38. Tina Scares away the Snow Monster

Tina enjoyed skiing in the mountains. She enjoyed sliding up and down the snow-covered mountain. She would often put on skis and slide down mountain slopes with her father and friends. One day, Tina was playing music on her iPod and skiing in a remote part of the mountain, when she saw something big and hairy moving towards her. It was a snow monster! She had never seen a snow monster before. The snow monster was big and ferocious. She was scared. She didn't know what to do as she trembled in fear. Tina was fearful but she thought over what to do. Suddenly, she had an idea. She quickly raised the volume of the music. The monster stopped still in its tracks. It had never heard such strange sounds! Scared, the monster ran in the opposite direction. Tina escaped unscathed because of her quick wit and unusual idea.

39. The Honest Weaver

There lived a poor weaver in a village. The weaver was honest and hard-working. He bought cotton every day and wove it into cloth. He led a simple life. One day, the weaver had left the cotton out in the veranda. The naughty wind blew it away. The weaver ran behind it, but the wind took it farther and farther away. The poor weaver was worried. He had purchased the cotton with his hard-earned money. Finally, the wind stopped blowing. The weaver saw that there was a big heap of cotton. The wind said, "Which cotton is yours?" The weaver replied, "I cannot say which one is mine, but I do know how much is mine. I will take that much and go." The wind was so pleased with his honesty that it gifted him the entire heap of cotton! Honesty pays. We must always be honest.

40. The Playful Monkeys

Susan loved animals. Whenever she found an opportunity, she would offer food to animals. One day, Susan decided to visit the river for a swim. Her elder sister, Carol, also went along with her to the river. There lived monkeys near the river-bank. Susan carried a small paper bag with her. There was some food inside the paper bag. She said, "I will give this leftover food to the monkeys." "Be careful with the monkeys!" Carol said. "Monkeys are playful. They will play pranks and might hurt you," she warned her younger sister Susan. When they reached the river, Susan forgot all about her sister's warning. She started throwing food at the monkeys. The monkeys began crowding around her. More and more monkeys kept coming. Susan was scared! She finally threw all the food in the paper bag at the monkeys, and managed to escape. Since then, she always followed her sister's advice.

41. Queen Grace

Queen Grace loved people in her kingdom. She always thought of helping the poor people. Once, a wise wizard came to see Queen Grace on her birthday. He gifted the Queen with a chest on her birthday. He said, "This chest will bring peace and happiness whenever opened with generosity." "Wow! This is a wonderful chest," the Queen exclaimed in surprise. So, Queen Grace travelled around and gathered the most generous people before she opened the chest. However, nothing happened. Then, Queen Grace met a poor girl, who asked her for the chest. At first, the Queen hesitated, but on seeing how poor the girl was, she gave it to her. When the girl opened it, a bright light shone. The girl turned into a wizard and said, "Why look for it in others? Generosity starts within yourself!" Thus, Queen Grace's kingdom was filled with peace and happiness.

42. Don't Reveal a Secret

Once upon a time, a hare, a squirrel and a deer were great friends. They lived and frolicked together. They enjoyed life. As good friends, they shared secrets. Good friends should not tell their secrets to others. One day, the hare and the squirrel found a tree full of apples. "We can all enjoy the apples, but you must keep it a secret," the hare and the squirrel decided. Then they met the deer and told him the secret because the deer was their friend. The deer promised not to tell anyone about the apple tree. But when they came to the riverside, the deer told all the animals present there about the tree's apples. They all went to the tree and ate its apples. The hare and the squirrel were very angry with the deer. They said, "We cannot be friends with you, as you did not keep the secret." The deer was sad, but he learnt his lesson.

43. Who is the More Beautiful?

Once upon a time, there was a ladybird and a butterfly. They were friends but the butterfly was too proud of her beauty. The ladybird was fed up with the butterfly for showing off about her beauty all the time. One day, the ladybird said, "You think you are the most beautiful, but everyone does not think so." The butterfly said, "I am more beautiful than you. If there is a beauty contest, I will win the contest. If you are ready for the challenge, then let us participate in the beauty contest." So, a beauty contest was held. The jury members were worms and beetles. All of them said, "We vote for the helpful ladybird. She is beautiful within and outside." The butterfly felt humiliated by the shocking result. The ladybird said, "It is not our physical looks, but good behaviour that matters." Butterfly said sorry to the ladybird. They became friends again.

44. The Value of Patience

Once, there lived a kind king. His name was Arnold. Everyone spoke about the kindness of King Arnold. He had no children. He treated a farmer's son like his own child. He taught the farmer's son everything necessary to be a good ruler. But the boy had one weakness. He did not have the patience to wait. King Arnold wanted to teach him the importance of patience. So, the king took him to the edge of the forest. Through the trees, they could see a treasure box. The king instructed, "You have to wait till afternoon. Once the sun is overhead, you can enter the forest and get back the treasure." King Arnold left after instructing. The farmer's son was tempted to enter the forest at once, but managed to wait. Finally, at noon, he entered the forest and got the treasure. The king was pleased. The farmer's son had learnt patience.

45. Magic Pot for Food

There was an orphanage with lots of children. The children in the orphanage suffered from malnutrition. They were not given sufficient food to eat. The children were sad. The children in the orphanage did not know what to do. They could only pray to God for more food. One night, little Tommy and Jimmy were sleepless. So, the boys got up and decided to take a walk outside in the star-lit night. "Look there, a pot!" said Tommy, pointing towards a tree. The boys ran to it and saw inside. The pot was empty. The boys were disappointed because there was no food in it. Sadly, Jimmy felt inside the pot. There were some leftovers of mashed potatoes in the pot. Suddenly, the pot shook. In a few seconds it was brimming with cooked rice and mashed potatoes. The boys had a wonderful dinner from the magic pot. They never lacked food again.

46. Thieves and the Brave Girl

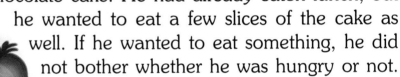

Amelia was a very brave and intelligent girl. She could face any problem because she was intelligent. She was honest and wanted everyone to be honest. One day, Amelia was at a toy store when she saw a man stealing money from the cash counter while no one was looking. Amelia decided to catch the thief. She could not fight him because he was big. So, she made an intelligent plan. Amelia followed the man to a small cafe. He and his friends sat down to count the stolen money. Amelia understood that the other men were also thieves. They had come together to share their earnings. She saw a policeman near by. She thought this was the best opportunity to catch them. Amelia raised her voice and shouted, "Help, I have been robbed by those men!" The policeman was alarmed. He rushed to help Amelia. He caught the thieves after chasing them.

47. Ted Gave Food to Poor Children

Ted loved pastries, chocolates and cakes. He ate them whenever he wanted to. Often, he ate more than he should eat at his age. Ted's mother baked new delicacies for him to eat. One day, Ted's mother baked a delicious chocolate cake. He had already eaten lunch, but he wanted to eat a few slices of the cake as well. If he wanted to eat something, he did not bother whether he was hungry or not. He just ate. But today, he did not want to be greedy. 'I should not be greedy,' he thought. Suddenly, he remembered that there were poor children at a nearby orphanage. 'They would be happy if they ate this cake,' Ted thought. With his mother's permission, he gave them the cake. 'It feels so much better to see them enjoying the cake, than it is to eat it myself,' Ted thought as he smiled.

48. Linda and the Beautiful World

Everyone loves to see falling snowflakes. Linda especially loved the snowflakes as they fell gently. It was like a beautiful dream. One day, it was snowing lightly. The snowflakes were falling gently. Linda could not resist the temptation to enjoy the day out in the open. She stepped out with her Aunt Celia to enjoy the day. "Dear Aunt Celia! See how beautiful the snowflakes look." Linda remarked as she played in the snow-covered garden. "Dear child Linda! Each snowflake is as lovely as it can be. But do you know a secret about snowflakes?" Celia asked. "No, dear Aunt Celia! Tell me what the secret is," Linda questioned. "Each snowflake has a unique pattern. It is one of its kind," Aunt Celia said. Linda was amazed. "Though snowflakes are all different yet they are all so beautiful," she remarked. "Yes", said Ant Celia, "We live in this beautiful world."

49. Don't be Afraid of Rainstorm

Ryan was scared of thunder and lightning. Whenever it rained heavily accompanied by lightning and thunder, he would look away and hide. He hated lightning and thunder. One day he was playing in the park when the wind began to blow, and leaves from the trees fell on the ground. Ryan feared the worst. He thought thunder and lightning could strike any time. Ryan ran to Emma, her baby-sitter. "My dear Ryan! There is a rainstorm brewing. It might begin raining anytime now. Let us take shelter in the gazebo there," Emma said. Emma did not want to take any chance. She wanted to run to safety as quickly as possible. She ran towards the shelter with Ryan. As they waited for the storm to pass, Emma explained how storms happen. Soon, Ryan understood that he should not panic at thunderstorms! He should be careful but not afraid of it.

50. *Margaret Learns to Use the Pen*

Margaret loved writing. She used a pencil to write and doodle. She would then run around showing everyone her doodles. One day, she saw a pen on her father's desk. She loved this pen. It looked beautiful. She would keep staring at the pen greedily wanting to write with it. One day, she asked, "Father, you have a lovely pen. I want to write with this pen. "This pen is unlike other pens and your pencil. You may not like using it," he said. Margaret replied that she would like to try anyway. "You have to dip this pen in ink before writing every word. It is an old-fashioned pen," he said. Margaret's hands were soon covered with ink! Using the pen was more difficult than she had thought. She asked her father to teach her how to use it. After a few weeks, she finally learnt to write with it.

51. *Defeating the Cruel Dragon*

Prince Arthur was a brave prince. He always worked for the welfare of his subjects. In his kingdom, there lived a cruel dragon. He had created havoc in the whole kingdom. Prince Arthur decided to defeat the dragon. A knight who had heard about the cruel dragon also decided to fight with the dragon and defeat him. Both of them set out to

fight against the dragon to end his cruelty. They wanted to fight and defeat the cruel dragon on their own so that they might boast about it. So, they took separate paths. When Prince Arthur reached the dragon's lair, the dragon blew his fiery breath and nearly killed him. The same happened with the knight. Then, they realised that to defeat the cruel dragon, they would have to unite. They decided to work together. With their combined intelligence and strength, they defeated the cruel dragon easily.

52. Own up Your Mistake

Claire was a small boy. He was disciplined. Once he made a mistake. Everyone makes a mistakes sometimes. Even disciplined boys can make mistakes but it is important to own up the mistake. One day, Claire fell ill but no one knew the reason. Sitting by his bedside, his grandfather told him a story. "When I was your age, one day, I accidentally broke my mother's cookie jar. I did not tell anyone. The guilt made me feel sick." "What is guilt, grandpa?" Claire asked.

"Guilt is the feeling when you make a mistake and feel bad about it," grandpa said. "How did you get well, grandpa?" asked Claire. "By owning up my mistake, I became free of guilt!" said grandpa. Claire started crying and said, "I lost the pen I had borrowed from you. I am so sorry!" "See, you have owned up your mistake. Now, you have no guilt. You will get well soon, my child!" said grandpa.

53. Red Shoes for Jane

It was a cold night in winter. Jane was sleeping in her room. Suddenly, a traveller knocked at Jane's door. The traveller looked old, tired and sick. She allowed the traveller to come in. She looked after the traveller and nursed him. The traveller was about to die. On his death bed, he gave Jane a pair of red shoes and said, "They will keep you safe, my child." Jane did not believe him but accepted the gift anyway. It was winter and Jane was poor. So, she decided to wear the red shoes. One night, Jane opened the door and saw a ferocious tiger sitting outside. Before she knew what was happening, brightly shining rays came out of the red shoes, straight at the tiger. The tiger was scared. It ran off at once, and never came back. Now Jane understood the value of the gift, the traveller gave.

54. *Hard Work Means Good Fortune*

Clarence was an intelligent boy. His father was a carpenter. He was good at his work, and worked very hard. Clarence saw his father working very hard. He used to think, if his father was rich, he would not have to work hard. One day, a strange looking man came to his father's shop. The man smiled and said, "Good fortune awaits you! I can see it written in your face." Saying so, he left the shop. Clarence was watching everything with complete attention. He was happy and said, "Father, this means you will not have to work anymore!" His father laughed. He told Clarence, "My boy, this is a lesson for you. Good fortune is for those who work hard and honestly. We make our own future by working hard. The day we decide to be lazy, all our fortunes will disappear." Clarence never forgot this lesson!

55. *Loads of Ice-cream*

Benjamin loved ice-cream. Whenever he went out visiting with his parents, he forced his parents to treat him to ice-cream. He used to remind his father to bring ice-cream

when he came back home from office. His mother often told him not to eat too many ice-creams, but Benjamin never listened. One day, Benjamin heard the tinkle of the ice-cream truck. He raced outdoors and ran to the ice-cream seller. There were loads of ice-cream. After eating a Vanilla Cone and a Choco-bar, Benjamin ate full chocolate ice-cream fudge. He did not want to eat anything now. He was so full. 'What a good way to spend my pocket money!' Benjamin thought. Soon his mother said, "Benjamin, Aunt Mary has called us for tea right now. She's making your favourite tarts." But Benjamin was too full to eat! Now, he knew that it never pays to be greedy.

56. The Courage to be Different

Melinda loved to read and learn new things. She did not like to play all the time. The other children thought she was different. They laughed and made fun of her. She did not like others making fun of her. Melinda did not know what to do about it. But when she saw a dancing swan, she found the answer. One afternoon, Melinda saw a crowd gathered by the lake at the park. Moving closer, she saw the group was watching a small swan dancing by herself. A person said, "The other swans may be beautiful but this one is courageous. Look how confidently she is dancing." Melinda understood that the dancing swan stood out because it had the courage to be different. From that day onwards, Melinda did not worry about the other children laughing at her. She did not pay attention to their comments. Now she became a strong and confident girl.

57. The Greedy Tolstoy Tom

Tolstoy Tom was a greedy tom-cat. He roamed about here, there and everywhere in search of left-over foodstuff. When he found nothing anywhere, he would wait for hours for the neighbours to place their trash outside. He would slurp tasty tit-bits from it. Eating infected left-over food often made him sick. Many a time he needed to be taken to the vet. But Tolstoy Tom never learnt his lesson. One day, he found a group of alley cats eating away from the trash can. 'Oh, this is the best opportunity for me. I must join them,' thought Tolstoy Tom. He snuggled up to them as usual to grab a bite to eat. When the alley cats saw him, they began to chase him. Tolstoy Tom ran for safety. With great difficulty, he found a place to hide. From then on, Tolstoy Tom stopped being greedy for food.

58. Real Magic is Kindness

Valencia was a kind girl. She was always helpful to others. She was cheerful and wanted everyone to be cheerful. She often gave flowers to old people living in a home near by, thinking it would cheer them up. They would smile back at Valencia and bless her. One day, she was plucking flowers to take home when she saw an unusual rose. It was pink with the shades of purple. It was big and beautiful. The flower appeared to smile. As she carried the rose back home, she decided to give it to Mr. Gladstone, as he was quite unwell. To her amazement, the rose turned red with the shades of yellow when he held it. At the same time, Mr. Gladstone was magically cured! Everyone was amazed to see the effect of the magic rose, but Mr. Gladstone said, "The real magic is Valencia's kindness." Everyone understood that kindness can heal.

59. Martin's Kindness Won Him Friends

Martin was a kind-hearted boy. He loved birds. He was very kind towards them. He always fed them with kindness. Crows and sparrows came to his terrace. He never forgot to give them the pieces of food. One day, Martin saw a beautiful brown swallow hop on to his terrace. Martin had left bread crumbs for the birds to feed on. The swallow saw the bread crumbs he had left and ate them. Then, it hopped towards Martin and said, "Martin, thank you so much for the tasty bread crumbs." Martin was surprised. "You can talk. How do you know my name?" asked Martin. "All the birds know your name and they told me about your kindness. I am a magic swallow, so I can talk to humans," said the bird. Martin was thrilled. He had never imagined that his kindness would make birds his friends!

60. Obey Your Mother

Darwin was a little boy. He was always playful. Every day, he visited the park to play. When he played in the park, he did not want to come back. His mother often warned him not to play after sunset. Darwin never listened. One evening, he was playing with his friend Mark. It was already late. Darwin and his friend Mark decided to ride the see-saw. Unfortunately, it had rained and the see-saw got stuck in the mud. Darwin was high up in the air. Mark tried to push the see-saw down, but the see-saw would not budge. As it was past playtime, the park was lonely. The two boys began to weep loudly. Fortunately, the park watchman heard them crying. He was just closing the park gate. Now, he came running to help them. Finally, he helped the boys out of the see-saw. From then onwards, Darwin always obeyed his mother.

61. Gratitude from the Butterfly

Frank loved butterflies. He would watch multi-coloured butterflies for hours. He would never hurt them even when he chased butterflies. His uncle, Samuel, caught butterflies to study them. Whenever Uncle Samuel went to catch butterflies, Frank would also go with him. One day, Frank saw a colourful butterfly trapped into Uncle Samuel's net. Frank felt sorry for the poor creature and released it. Uncle Samuel did not see him doing it. The butterfly came up to his ear and whispered, "Thank you, little boy." Frank was amazed. "Wow! This beautiful butterfly can also talk," he thought. Frank felt happy that he had saved the butterfly. He also felt happy to discover that the butterfly could talk just like him. He disliked Uncle Samuel for catching butterflies. Having received gratitude from the talking butterfly, he never failed to be kind to all animals and birds.

62. Kindness Brings More Kindness

Georgina always helped poor people. She did not want to see anyone sad. One day, Georgina found a woman begging in the market. "Please help me. I have six children and they have not eaten for days," the woman was begging. Georgina felt sorry for her. She bought a large loaf of bread and followed the woman to her house. "Please have this loaf of bread for your children and for you," she requested. The woman thanked Georgina. She divided the loaf in two, and went out with it. When she came back, Georgina asked her where she had gone. She said, "I went to give half the bread to my neighbours. They are hungry, too." Georgina was surprised. She thought, 'How wonderful! Even though she was hungry yet this kind woman thought of helping out others first.' From that day on, Georgina began helping needy people even more than she did earlier.

63. Always be Happy

Henry was always sad. He thought he worked very hard, but earned very little. He did not know what to do. He wanted to earn more money. One day, he met his friend Peter. He told Peter he wanted to earn more but did not know how to do so. Suddenly, Peter snatched Henry's wallet with money in it and ran away. Henry was shocked. He also ran after Peter to catch him. Peter had gone very far leaving Henry very sad. After an hour, Peter came back and returned the wallet. At this, Henry felt very happy. Peter said, "You are very happy now because you got your money. But you were not happy with the same amount of money in your wallet earlier. Money does not bring happiness." Henry understood that happiness means being happy always from the heart. From then, he focused on working hard, rather than complaining about not earning enough.

64. Melissa's Violin

Once upon a time, a wizard gifted a violin to a queen. The violin did not produce nice music. The queen tried to tune the instrument, but it did not work. She thought that the violin was useless and threw it away. A poor little girl, Melissa, was going across the street. She found the violin the queen had thrown away. She picked it up, thinking, 'This is a wonderful violin. I will keep it and play beautiful music with it every day.' Melissa's fascination with the violin was getting stronger every day. She played it for months and years. Finally, one day, the violin started playing the most beautiful melodies. Everyone started talking about Melissa and her melodious violin. The queen was surprised. She asked the wizard about it. "This magical violin produces beautiful music when you love it, and put your interest in it," the wizard said. The queen was ashamed of her mistake.

65. Intelligence is Better than Beauty

Magdalene was a fairy. She was not so beautiful as other fairies. Many of her classmates in the fairy school made fun of her. But she was intelligent. She did not fight with her friends even when they made fun of her. One day, some wizards attacked fairyland. He put all the fairies in prison. Intelligent Magdalene put a spell on her clothes. After putting the spell, she looked like a witch. 'I must save the other fairies. I must follow the wizards to save my friends,' Magdalene thought as she went after the wizard. The wizards were dancing and singing to celebrate the victory. Magdalene easily slipped in, disguised as a witch. While the party was in full swing, she set all the fairies free and they trapped the wizards inside their den. From that day on, all the fairies respected Magdalene for her intelligence. They said sorry to Magdalene.

66. Smiling Photos

Alisa loved going to school. She listened to everything that her teacher said. She followed the words of her teacher and did her home work on time. Alisa's teacher gave the class a new home work. She instructed students to bring happiness to people. All the students handed over their home work in time except Alisa. She had also done the home work but in a different way. She gave her teacher a small box instead. The teacher was surprised. She smiled as she opened the box. At that moment, Alisa clicked a photo. In the box, the teacher found many photos. Each photo showed the smiling faces of different people. The teacher showed the photos to the class. The children smiled as they saw those photos. Alisa immediately clicked the class photo showing the smiling children. Alisa got an 'A' grade.

67. 'Please' and 'Thank you'

Tim was a pleasant child with good manners. Everyone loved him because he respected elders. Tim loved Nature. He liked to visit parks and forests. One evening, Tim was walking through a park. He saw a huge tree in the park. The sign board on the tree read: "I am a magic tree. Say the magic words and you will see." Tim was surprised as he read the sign board. Tim spoke the magic words: "Abracadabra, Woogly Toogly, Magicalious…!" Nothing happened. He repeated the magic words again, but nothing happened. Giving up, he said, "Please, dear tree! Help me." Suddenly, a big door opened in the trunk. A sign read: "Carry on with the magical words!" Tim said, "Thank you, dear tree!" There were a number of toys and sweets inside the trunk. Tim understood why people always say that 'Please' and 'Thank you' are magic words!

68. *Everything Has a Purpose*

Once, there stood an old church high up on a hill. The church attracted people from nearby places. A visit to the church made them peaceful in heart and mind. The visitors prayed at the church and heard the pastor's sermons. There hung a bell outside the Church. The bell chimed melodiously every day. Every day when it was time for the sun to rest and for the moon to rise, the pastor of the church would ring the bell. The bell hated when it was rung. The bell did not like to be disturbed. He complained to the pastor. The pastor explained, "Everything has its purpose and yours is to let the people of the nearby town know it's time for them to go home and rest. Hearing you, children know that their parents will come home soon. Your sound brings happiness to many." Now the bell knew its purpose and never complained again.

69. *Lucy Loves the Cat*

Little Lucy loved the cats. She would go out of way to take care of the abandoned cats. One day, she found an abandoned cat. She would not leave her alone. She thought others would not look after her properly. Lucy had to visit the library. She carried the cat to the library. At the library, Miss Roselyn, the librarian, checked her basket and exclaimed, "No cats in the library! She does not know any rules. You have to take her back." Lucy pleaded, "Miss Roselyn, my cat just lost her mother and is very sad. I have already told her about all the library rules. Please let her in." Miss Roselyn felt sorry and said, "Very well. She can stay with me at the desk until you are ready to leave." Lucy thanked Miss Roselyn, leaving the cat with her. The cat also mewed to thank her.

70. Daniel and Air Bubbles

Daniel loved food. Daniel ate almost anything. He had no choice or taste. His mother was worried about him. She did not like him eating up anything that he was offered. His mother had warned him time and again that it was not good to eat anything that he found strange, funny or attractive, but Daniel would not listen! Hubert was the boy who lived in the neighbourhood. One day, Hubert was blowing soap bubbles. The round and shining soap bubbles gently wafted in the air. They rose up in the air, stayed for a while and then disappeared. Daniel saw those bubbles. They were flying attractively in the air. Daniel opened his mouth, gulped in one soap bubble, then a few more! Soon, his mouth tasted of soap. He was feeling the bad taste. He disliked it! Now he wished he had listened to his mother's warnings.

71. Monster in the Bed

Jonas was an intelligent boy. He was also very imaginative. Every day, he would tell his mother about the monsters that lived under his bed. One day, Jonas woke up with red eyes. "What happened to your eyes, Jonas? Why are they red?" his mother asked. "The monster didn't let me sleep, momma," Jonas said. The mother liked his creativity. But she felt worried that Jonas was up all night. So, she made a plan. The next night when Jonas went to bed he saw a faint light under his bed. 'Could it be a monster?' he thought. Jonas was now convinced that a monster lived under his bed. When he peeped under the bed, he saw a torch and a note, "Dear Jonas, we are tired of playing the monster game. It is late; go to bed!" Jonas felt very foolish, and went to sleep at once!

72. *The Fun of Reading*

Nathan, a young boy, loved listening to stories. But he hated reading the stories. Every week, the postman brought Nathan's favourite magazine. The magazine carried adventurous stories. He would love the magazine and ask everyone to read some stories out of it. He got this week's magazine today. He ran to his mother, requesting, "Momma! Please read out the stories to me." "Not now, Nathan. I am busy cooking." Nathan was disheartened but thought he would ask his elder sister and brother to read out the stories. So, he went to his sister and brother but they also refused, "Nathan, we are studying. You are big enough to read on your own." Nathan sighed, "No, listening is more fun!" But no one read out

the stories to Nathan. "I will try reading the stories on my own," Nathan decided. Nathan started reading on his own. Soon, reading became fun to him.

73. *The Entertainment Lamp*

Rosemary was a curious child who wanted to know everything. One day, she was helping her grandma arrange the cupboard. The cupboard was full of old objects. She observed each object with deep interest. Suddenly, Rosemary found an old lamp that looked beautiful. "Is it a magical lamp, grandma?" she asked. "No darling," said grandma, "but I call it my entertainment lamp!" "Entertainment lamp?" Rosemary was more surprised. "Yes, entertainment! This lamp will tell you stories just like a film theatre," grandma replied. Rosemary looked confused. Grandma smiled and said, "If you were to look into its dancing flames, you could come up with such fascinating stories, Rosemary! Look; sometimes the flames remind us of dragons, and other times, of warriors. Try it!" Rosemary loved the idea. Every evening, she sat with her grandma and told her stories based on the flickering light of the lamp! Grandma loved those stories.

74. The Poor Child

Winter is a difficult time for poor children. They don't have warm clothes. They pray to God for help. One day, a poor boy stood outside a shoe-store. It was very cold winter afternoon. He was praying to God, "O Lord of Heavens! Please give me a pair of shoes." While praying, the boy thought God could hear his words. He strongly felt that God would answer his prayers. A kind woman heard him and took him to the shoe-store. She placed a pair of new socks upon the boy's feet and also bought him a pair of shoes. Then the woman patted his back and said, "There you will feel more comfortable now!" The boy thanked her. As she turned to go, the boy caught her hand and asked with tears in his eyes, "Are you God's wife? "I'm His child just like you," said the woman, before leaving the store.

75. Wounds May not Show

There was a wise and kind emperor. He always thought about helping his subjects. He wanted to heal the wounds of people. He had a large number of servants and courtiers. But none of them could help him in the task he wanted to do. Finally, he

selected an assistant who could help him. He took his assistant to the balcony of the palace. "See my big kingdom! You must help me heal the wounds of people," the emperor said. His assistant asked, "Master, what must I remember if I am to carry out your wishes?" The emperor replied, "Look upon all the people as wounded." The curious assistant asked, "But why, my Lord?" The emperor explained, "Everyone is in pain in some way. Wounds may not show, but they are there. Discover people who are hurt, and you will finally understand them. Help them." The assistant understood what the wise emperor wanted.

76. Real Partners

A great scientist worked with a study partner. They were like friends. A friend is the one who can tell your mistakes on your face. One day, the study partner stopped working as he became sick. The scientist became sad. He could not work without his friend. Some of his students sent him a new study partner. Two weeks later, the scientist became sad again. His students asked, "Sir, what happened?" He said, "My new study partner is very intelligent. He says 'yes' to everything I say. He gives me ten reasons to show that I am right. My old study partner was different. If I was wrong, he said it on my face and gave many reasons to show I was wrong. I don't want someone who will agree with me blindly. I want a partner who will help me work better by showing mistakes." So, he himself chose a partner.

77. Karen Must Work

Karen did not like to work. She avoided doing housework. She never cleaned her cupboard or brushed her shoes. The mother wanted her to take interest in extra activities, if she did not like doing household activities. Karen's mother took her to a curio store. "Karen, there are so many items that something or the other is bound to interest you. Choose any thing that you like," the mother said. Karen saw a brush. It was old but very cheap. "This is a magic brush. It cleans the room really well," said the store-keeper. Karen excitedly bought the brush. When she got home, she found the brush very ordinary. She complained to the store-keeper that there was no magic in the brush. He said "Little girl, the brush works like magic but you have also to make efforts at your end." Karen understood that unless she worked, nothing would work wonders.

78. Avoid Troubles

Josephine was a wonderful fairy. Nearly everything was good about her. She was beautiful, curious and helpful. But there was one weakness in her. She poked her nose in other people's life. This often brought her troubles. So, the king of fairies decided to teach her a lesson. He placed a big box in the palace courtyard. "No one should open this box of troubles," he commanded. Josephine didn't listen to the king fairy. She was too curious to wait. Josephine opened the box. Soon, a lot of imps jumped out of the box and ran around. Josephine ran after them. The imps pulled her hair and pushed her around. She fell down and scraped her knee. Finally, Josephine said, "I am so sorry to interfere in others' business. I will never do it again." The king of fairies heard her and called the imps to leave her alone.

79. Everything Has a Reason

Henrietta was intelligent and curious. She always wanted to learn and understand anything she found strange. She felt satisfied only when she understood the reason. There was a low stone wall in her village. Henrietta often looked at this low stone wall in her village and asked her mother, "What is the use of this wall? Why was it built?" Her mother answered wisely, "Henrietta, there must be a reason." She was not satisfied with her mother's answer and wanted to know the reason. One day, a flock of cattle from the neighbouring field was grazing there. As Henrietta watched, an evil bull charged at her. Henrietta screamed in fear, "Help me, someone!" Just then, she saw that the wall blocked the bull. He could not cross the wall. Henrietta ran home to her mother and said, "Mother! The wall saved my life! You were right. Everything has a reason."

80. Greed Causes Loss

There was a greedy farmer. He did not realise that greed is a bad quality. People want more because they are greedy. But they often end up losing because of greed. Once, the greedy farmer helped a fairy. So, she said, "I will give you all the land you can walk in a day. But you must come back to the starting point by sunset." The next morning, the farmer started walking quickly. He kept walking all afternoon. Then he realised, "I need to get back to the starting point by sunset." So, he quickly turned back. He ran fast because the sun was going to set soon. Soon, he was exhausted and could not reach the starting point. The fairy said, "You failed because of your greed. If you had turned back sooner, you would have had a lot of land." The farmer promised that he would not be greedy again.

81. The Fairy Who Gives Money

Tanya was a little girl. When her tooth was shaking for the first time, she cried in pain. It pained more in the night. "Ouch," cried Tanya in pain, "My tooth is shaking." "Don't worry," said her mother, "We will have the tooth pulled out." Tanya looked terrified. Mother pacified her, "Tanya, don't worry. The tooth fairy will leave money for you in return for your tooth." Tanya was excited at the thought of a reward from the tooth fairy. Tanya wanted to know more about the tooth fairy. So, she got her tooth extracted. At night, mother helped Tanya place the tooth carefully under the pillow. Tanya decided to stay up and wait for the tooth fairy, but no one came. Soon, her eyes drooped and she was fast asleep. In the morning, a 10-pound note lay under her pillow. "The tooth fairy actually came!" shouted Tanya, happily eyeing the money.

82. More Ways to Measure

Matthew loved visiting foreign nations and learning their ways. Matthew had arrived in China. He loved the Chinese tea and observed the Chinese tea-sellers. Their tea tasted different and he liked the way it was served. One evening, while walking along the market place in China, Matthew came across a tea-seller. The tea-seller was selling a bowl of tea for a certain amount of money. He measured the exact amount of tea using a cup so that the drinker might not get even an extra inch more than he had paid for. Matthew thought he would be clever, so he asked the tea-seller, "Could you sell me half a bowl of tea?" The tea-seller smiled as he took out a bowl and poured half of the tea from the other bowl into it. Matthew understood that there were more ways than one to measure the tea.

83. Football in Rain

Matt and his friends played football. Every weekend, they would assemble in the ground to play the game of football for hours. But they did not like the rainy season because they could not play football in rain. The rain showers sprayed down on the ground. Matt and the boys looked on in annoyance as they packed up their football kits. 'Another Saturday wasted!' they thought. The boys were about to go, when they heard a squishing sound on the football ground. It was Maher, a poor boy from their neighbourhood. He always watched them play but never joined in. As the boys looked on, Maher tossed the ball; his legs sloshed and splashed in the water. Matt said, "It looks like fun! Let's join him." Soon, they all joined Maher. After a fun-filled time, they all thanked Maher for showing them that football could be fun in the rain, too.

84. Fun at Beach

Patricia was a fun-loving girl. She never missed an opportunity to go out and have fun. She enjoyed going out on family picnics. Patricia was sad. She had just recovered from a nasty sickness and so had to miss her school picnic. She was looking for the next opportunity when she could go on a picnic. Her parents, however, had a surprise for her. She had a visit from her Uncle John, Aunt Linda and her cousins Julia and Cecelia. The two families piled into a wagon and set out for the beach. At the beach, her uncle and cousins played volleyball with Patricia. The children then went surf-boarding. At lunch, Patricia wolfed down homemade tuna sandwiches by her mother, while Aunt Linda had baked an apple pie, especially for her. 'Well, missing the picnic was not bad after all,' thought Patricia at the end of the day.

85. God Always Helps

Thomas loved adventure. He had been to several adventurous voyages. There is thrill in an adventure, but it has its price. Some adventures can be risky. Recently, Thomas had been on an adventurous voyage, when his ship sank. Thomas was the only survivor of the shipwreck and was washed up to a deserted island. He prayed to God for help but nothing happened. He managed to build a small hut over a few days. But one day, he returned from hunting to find his hut in flames and the smoke reaching the sky. "God, how could you do this to me?" he cried, stung with grief and anger. The next morning, Thomas woke up by the sound of a ship that was approaching the island. "How did you know I was here?" Thomas asked his rescuers. "We saw your smoke signal," the captain replied. Thomas learnt to trust God blindly.

86. Always Praise God

Old Ethel was saintly in nature. She thought everything good that happens is due to God. She stepped out of her house every morning and shouted, "Praise the Lord!" She did not care whether others liked her belief or not. Jen, Ethel's neighbour, was irritated with her morning practice. He complained several times that Ethel's blind faith would do her no good. But Ethel didn't care. One morning, Ethel shouted, "Praise the Lord! God, I have no food. Please provide for me!" Hours later, Ethel saw one big bag of groceries at her door. "Praise the Lord!" she screamed, "He has provided groceries for me!" Jen jumped out of the hedges and strongly replied, "It was not God! I bought those groceries! Would you stop shouting now?" Ethel shouted, "Praise God! He provided groceries and made you pay for them!" Jen was shocked! He decided to follow Ethel's morning practice.

87. William Loves Chocolates

William loved chocolates. Although he loved chocolates from everywhere yet he especially loved Swedish chocolates. His uncle lived in Sweden. He reminded his uncle to bring some chocolates whenever he came to visit them next time. William was excited to learn that Uncle John was coming from Sweden. Finally when he arrived, William was happy to see that he had brought a chocolate box with him. William hurriedly opened the box and he was disappointed to see the small size of the chocolates. "Uncle John, why are the chocolates so small in size? That is not very nice," he complained to his uncle. Uncle John laughed and said, "Well William, try one of the chocolates first." When William had a taste of the chocolate, it was the most delicious chocolate he had ever eaten. He understood that good things sometimes come in small packages. One should not judge quality by its size.

88. God's Ways are Unknown

Angela loved rock-climbing. She would often visit mountains to climb the tall peaks. Rock climbing is an adventurous sport but it requires courage to climb the tall peaks. Angela was courageous. One day, she went on yet another rock-climbing expedition. When she reached half the way to the top, the safety rope snapped against her eye and knocked out her contact lens. Angela searched desperately, hoping it had landed on a ledge. But it wasn't there. When she reached the top, she prayed to God, "You know exactly where my contact lens is. Please help me." As she walked down to the bottom, she met some new climbers and one of them shouted, "Hey! Did anybody lose a contact lens?" Angela found her contact lens. The climber who had her lens said, "Strangely, I saw an ant moving slowly across the rock, carrying it!" Angela thought, 'God has mysterious ways!'

89. The Fortune-teller's Prophecy

Mary studied in a boarding school. She was eagerly waiting for her birthday, when she would get gifts from so many people. One day, in a carnival, a fortune-teller prophesied, "Mary, you will get something beautiful and shiny on your birthday!" "Beautiful and shiny…? What could that be?" She tried to guess. Then, suddenly she realised happily, "I'll get a jewel on my birthday." She opened everyone's gifts excitedly. Sadly, there wasn't a single jewel in the packets. Her parents sent her a pretty dress and granny a colourful sweater. Aunt Martina had sent her shoes. Mary was disappointed. Just then, Sonia, her friend informed her, "Mary, a ball will be held in school." Mary looked at the gifts and squealed in delight, "Oh! The dress and the sweater are beautiful and the shoes are shiny! They are perfect for the coming ball! The fortune-teller was right."

90. The Tortoise Family Picnic

The tortoise is a slow animal. It works at a slow pace. It is slow but diligent. It can continue doing work for long without a break. It also needs to take rest for a while. Once, there lived a tortoise family. This family decided to go for a picnic. Being naturally slow, it took them seven years to reach the picnic spot. For the next six months, they cleaned the area and unpacked the picnic basket. However, they forgot to bring salt and pepper. "No one will eat until I return," said a young tortoise before leaving for home. The young tortoise did not return for several years. Then, the oldest tortoise started eating. It said, "I cannot control my hunger." The young tortoise suddenly appeared from behind a tree. It said, "I knew you wouldn't wait! So, I hid all along." Everyone in the family laughed.

91. Peaceful Life

Everyone wants to enjoy a peaceful life. Poor people think, if they had more money they would enjoy a peaceful and happy life. A fisherman, sitting under a tree near the

sea-shore, was poor but enjoying a peaceful and happy life. There came a rich merchant. The rich merchant passing by asked him, "Why are you not working?" The fisherman replied, "I've caught enough fish for today." The merchant scolded him, "Why don't you catch more fish instead of wasting your time?" The fisherman asked, "What will I gain by that?" "You will earn more money and buy a bigger boat!" "What will I do then?" "Catch more fish and earn even more money!" "Then what?" "You could become rich like me." "Then?" "You could enjoy your life peacefully!" "What do you think I'm doing right now?" the fisherman asked and the merchant was left speechless. He had no answer.

92. Reward and Punishment

Once, two angels, one old and the other young, came down to the world. The angels actually wanted to test the character of human beings. First, they chose a wealthy man. The angels decided to spend a night in a wealthy man's home. But he made them stay in the basement. There, the older angel sealed a hole in the wall. The next night, they rested at a poor man's house and he let them sleep on his bed. But his only cow was dead in the morning.

"Why punish him?" asked the younger angel. The older angel said, "I saw gold through that hole in the wealthy man's wall. As he is greedy, I sealed the wall, denying him gold. The angel of death came for the poor man's wife. I gave him the cow instead, saving the man's wife. Each got the due reward and punishment."

93. The Loyal Dog

Elizabeth was a brave girl, who enjoyed visiting the sea-side beach. She loved her pet dog Tom, who accompanied her wherever she went. One day, Elizabeth and Tom were together playing at the beach. She instructed her dog, "Tommy, please keep a watch over my things here. Meanwhile, I will go swimming in the sea." Tommy wagged his tail indicating he understood the instruction. Elizabeth was swimming in the sea when the rising waves overwhelmed her. They were very strong and she struggled to keep afloat. Elizabeth tried her best to swim against waves, but the waves engulfed her. Seeing her distress, Tom jumped into the water. He swam swiftly towards her. Elizabeth held onto Tom, who finally saved her. She was happy that her loyal friend did not abandon her in distress. As a special thank-you treat, she did not forget to give Tom, an extra doggy treat.

94. The Magical Cure

Jessica did not keep well. Only a fortnight ago, she had fallen terribly ill. The doctor gave her medicines, but she had not completely recovered even now. She did not enjoy taking bed-rest. She felt weak and upset. Every night before going to bed, she hoped she would completely recover tomorrow morning. She used to pray to God while going to sleep, "Dear God, please take away my illness and make me healthy and happy again!" Every morning she awoke feeling weak and ill. One night, as Jessica went to sleep, she had a miracle dream. She saw a fountain of magical, sparkling water. Jessica dipped her hand in the magical fountain and immediately felt better. She woke up soon after, feeling refreshed and happy. She never told anyone about her dream, but she knew that the fountain of dreams had cured her!

95. Charles Loves Boating

Charles loved boating. Every evening, he and his father would row across the river. Charles's father never allowed him to go boating on his own. Every evening, he waited

for his father to come. If he came late, Charles would want to run alone to the river for boating. One day, Charles' father said that he was very busy that day. He asked Charles not to go alone for the boat-ride. But Charles became restless by evening and decided to go alone. He was thrilled as the boat glided across the river. After a while, the boat got stuck in seaweed. Then, it started to rain. Charles panicked. He did not know what to do. Luckily, his father came looking for him. He rescued him. Charles had never been more relieved in his life. "I am sorry, dad. I promise I will never go boating again," Charles said. The father was happy.

96. Elves Love Lydia's Stories

Lydia loved to write stories. She wrote wonderful stories about dragons, fairies and princes, and read them aloud in her garden. She would forget everything while writing. She only wished, if she could write in colourful letters. One day, she found a pen in the garden. To her amazement, the pen could write in seven colours. When she wrote with it, her stories seemed to come alive. The stories became colourful. She enjoyed reading those stories aloud even more now. She continued writing with this pen every day. One day, she found that there was no ink in the pen. "Oh no! Where will I get magical ink from?" she wondered. Next morning, she found a little ink pot on her window-sill. There was a note: "From all the garden elves. We love your stories!" Lydia was thrilled and thanked the garden elves by writing many new stories just for them!

97. A Piano for Maria

Maria had talent for music. She could play the piano like an accomplished musician. But she was not very confident about herself. Her parents owned a music store. Whenever she found time, she went to the store and played the piano. As she was under-confident, she used to say, "I want to be a musician, but don't think I am good enough." One day, Maria was excited to see a big brown piano for her in store. Maria had never played such a big piano before. When she played it, everyone stopped to listen. Soon, people started flocking to the music shop just to hear Maria play the piano. Slowly, she became more confident. She thought, 'It was only my fear that was holding me back.' She continued to practise on the new piano every day. Each day, she became more and more confident. One day, she became a famous musician!

98. Every Problem Has a Solution

Magdalene loved to cook. She learnt new recipes from anyone who could teach her. One day, Magdalene was thrilled to learn to bake a cake from her Aunt Alexia. She was now confident that she could bake a cake, all by herself. One day, Magdalene put together all the ingredients and placed the cake in the oven. 'I am sure it will be perfect!' Magdalene thought. Just as she was about to set the timer, the oven stopped working. Magdalene was very sad. Aunt Alexia understood the situation and said, "Even the most difficult challenge can be overcome if one thinks hard enough. Every problem also has a solution." Then, she put the cake mix in milk and boiled it. It made for a lovely dessert. Magdalene learnt a lesson and another recipe! Now whenever Magdalene landed in a problem, she remembered the words of Aunt Alexia, "Every problem has a solution."

99. Nicole's Golden Flower

Nicole loved her mother. She presented her mother flowers whenever she could. She was looking for a special flower to present to her mother. She was in the garden gathering flowers for her mother. 'I wish there were golden flowers! They would shine in the sunlight and look so magical,' she thought. Nicole looked for the flower everywhere but could not find that magical flower. Finally, when she came home, she started making paper flowers. She painted each petal of the paper flowers in beautiful golden colour. They looked just as beautiful as she had imagined! Then she added the golden flowers to the bouquet she had prepared for her mother. "I have never seen such a lovely bunch of flowers in my life, Nicole," declared mother with a smile. Even after the other flowers had dried up, the golden flowers in the vase on her mother's desk, appeared sparkling bright.

100. James and the Dwarf

James never ventured alone in the forest. But today, he unfortunately entered into the forest having lost his way while coming home. He was feeling thirsty when he approached a river-bank. Just as he was about to drink some water, a voice called out, "Stop! Don't drink that water!" The voice was that of a dwarf who was often friendly. James looked at the dwarf standing near a tree. "Why can't I drink water?" asked James. "The fairies are cleaning the river today," said the dwarf, "If you want fresh water, you must collect dew from flowers." James thanked the dwarf and started collecting dew. He shared the dew with the dwarf and said, "You helped me by telling me how to get fresh water. This is the only way I can pay you back for it!" The dwarf was pleased and helped James find his way out of the forest.

101. Emma's Bad Habit

Emma was a sweet little girl, who loved candies. No matter how many candies she ate, she always wanted to have some more. She had the bad habit of popping even thrown-away candies into her mouth. Her mother often warned her, "Emma! You're going to spoil your health, if you keep popping candies from the road." She did not pay attention to the warning. One day, Emma was playing with her friends when she saw something like candy lying in dust. 'Huh, looks like a candy!' thought Emma in glee. "Pop," and she had swallowed it. At night, she was rushed to the doctor when she complained of a severe stomach pain. "What's the metal-like object I see in your X-ray picture?" asked the doctor. The doctor immediately operated upon Emma and removed a coin from her stomach! Emma was so scared that she never ate things from the road again.

102. The Snowman Who Talked

Matthew and Mary played together in winters. They made snow houses and snowmen. One day, Matthew and Mary looked at their snowman admiringly. They could almost hear him breathing. They wished the snowman could talk to them. "Would you like to play with me?" the snowman said suddenly. Matthew and Mary almost dropped their jaws in astonishment. They couldn't believe what they just heard. "Yippee," chorused the children. The children spent the whole day playing and sharing stories with the snowman. At night, the snowman guarded the house. The next day, the children woke up to find sunlight streaming into their room. "It's a nice warm day. We can stay out longer," cried Mary. But when they ran out, the snowman was gone! The children were quite disappointed. There was just a puddle of water, and a note which said: "I will be back next year, Your Snowman."

103. Isabelle's Secret in Shed

Isabelle was a little girl who loved to play with pets. Naomi was her best friend. Naomi shared all her secrets with Isabelle. Isabelle also had a secret. She did not share her secret with anyone in the beginning. She wanted to wait for the right time to share the secret. Finally, she decided to share her secret with Naomi. "Come with me," she said to Naomi. The two girls went to the corner of the garden. There, nearly hidden by the tall grass, was an old shed. "What is that sound?" asked Naomi. Isabelle pointed near the door. There were five beautiful little kittens huddled together! "Our cat Molly had kittens," said Isabelle, "Mother says they are old enough now to go to new homes. Would you like one?" Naomi was thrilled. She chose the cutest one. Naomi thanked Isabelle. Their friendship grew deeper since then.

104. Gregory Loves Astronomy

Gregory was a curious boy. He would be filled with wonder looking at the blue sky. He wondered at the sparkling stars. He had too many questions. He knew only Uncle Anthony, an astronomer, would be able to answer his questions. "Why is the sky blue?" Gregory asked his Uncle Anthony. He explained, "Sunlight is made up of all the colours of the rainbow. But when sunlight passes through the air around the earth, only blue light can be seen most clearly. That is why the sky seems blue!" "Why do stars twinkle?" asked Gregory the next day. Uncle Anthony said, "Come; I will answer all your questions." He took Gregory to a planetarium and taught him all about the sun, planets, stars and the galaxy. Gregory enjoyed the visit. He was delighted. He told Uncle Anthony, "When I grow up, I want to be an astronomer, just like you!"

105. Charlie Loves Gardening

Charlie loved his garden. He wanted to learn about every plant in his garden. He would watch the gardener tending to plants every day. He wanted to work in the garden. One day, Charlie asked the gardener, "What are you planting?" "A rose plant," replied the gardener. Soon, small shoots sprouted. Charlie was excited. He watched those shoots and danced in joy. Every morning he would examine the plant to see how much it had grown. Every time it had grown a little. 'So, it grows at night. I will keep a watch,' thought Charlie. That night, he opened his window and looked, but he could not see anything, and soon fell asleep. The next morning, to his surprise, he saw a small bud on the plant. The gardener explained, "A plant grows slowly, but steadily, just like us!" Charlie was thrilled, and started helping in the garden every day.

106. Helen Makes Soup

Helen enjoyed cooking. She loved to watch her momma make the varieties of dishes. She was a little girl. So, her mother admonished her to keep away from fire. But her elder brother, Patric, encouraged her to experiment with cooking. One day, Helen found a red pot in the attic of her new house. She ran down with the pot to show it to her brother. "Isn't it beautiful?" asked Helen. Patric and Helen took the pot out into the garden. They then gathered some bricks, placed some twigs in between and lit a small fire. They filled the pot with water and placed it on the hearth. For fun they dropped some carrots and beetroots into the water and a pinch of salt.

Once the water boiled, Patric tasted it. It tasted lovely! The children then spent the whole summer preparing soup in their little red pot.

107. Todd Learns a Lesson

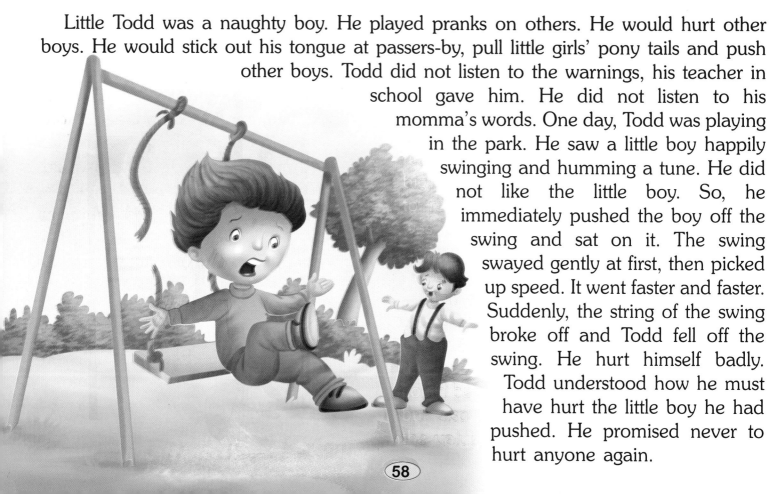

Little Todd was a naughty boy. He played pranks on others. He would hurt other boys. He would stick out his tongue at passers-by, pull little girls' pony tails and push other boys. Todd did not listen to the warnings, his teacher in school gave him. He did not listen to his momma's words. One day, Todd was playing in the park. He saw a little boy happily swinging and humming a tune. He did not like the little boy. So, he immediately pushed the boy off the swing and sat on it. The swing swayed gently at first, then picked up speed. It went faster and faster. Suddenly, the string of the swing broke off and Todd fell off the swing. He hurt himself badly. Todd understood how he must have hurt the little boy he had pushed. He promised never to hurt anyone again.

108. Children Missed the Sun

Children love to play in a park. Once, the sun shone brightly on the little park by the school. The children were happily running around, playing and singing. The bright sunshine made no difference to their enthusiasm. The sun shone brighter and stronger by each hour as children continued to play. Soon the children started sweating and blamed the sun. "We could have played more, if the day was not so warm. The sun has spoiled our fun," the children complained. The sun felt sad. It hid behind the clouds. It did not rise for two days. The children could not play because it was cloudy and grim. There was a nip in the air and everything looked grey. On the third day, the sun decided to come out and the children cheered. 'Oh, so they miss me, when I am not around,' thought the sun with a smile.

109. Tiffany's Extra Finger

Tiffany was a good-natured girl. She looked pretty much like the other girls in her class. But she looked very sad. All the others girls in the school used to make fun of her because she had six fingers. A tiny finger stuck out from her little finger, giving it two heads. Tiffany would look at her fingers and feel, "How awful it looks! I wish my fingers were like those of other girls." Tiffany's parents would console her, pointing out her good qualities. "You have beautiful hair, good manners and a sparkling smile. When you grow up, nobody will notice your finger and they will eventually stop teasing you," her mother said. Soon enough, Tiffany became very popular in school because she was good-natured and helpful. She had many other talents. Thus, Tiffany understood that physical features are not so important. It is more important to be a good person.

110. Trisha Goes Globe-trotting

Trisha was adventurous. She loved to read books on adventure. She looked in wonder at the many books in her grandfather's bookshelf. There were fat and thin books, books on sailors and their adventures on sea, books on the deep jungles in Africa, about kings and queens, fairies and witches. She had read nearly all of these books. Now she was looking for a new book to read. Trisha chose a book on the kingdoms of Asia and began to read about the great kings and the many wars fought there. Trisha was so fascinated that every day she would pick a book up on different continents to read about them. After reading them, she was motivated to visit those places. After her vacation when Trisha went back to school, her teacher asked her how she spent her holidays. "I went on a trip around the world," said Trisha enthusiastically.

111. Sandy in the Dragon Land

Sandy loved to play with gadgets. He was especially fascinated by the video games. The video games often brought him to wondrous lands inhabited by strange creatures. He would visit these lands without realising hours spent there. Sandy inserted a new CD into his video game player. He clicked 'Enter' and rolled on the moss-laden ground. As he got up, a hand reached from behind a tree and pulled him. "Sshh!" said the little girl. "Where are we?" asked Sandy surprised. "Dragon land," said the girl. Sandy heard a roar. A ball of fire whizzed in the air. Sandy and the girl rushed behind a bush. A green-winged creature, spouting fire, came into view. It was a ferocious dragon! Sandy felt a door under his feet. He looked down and saw the word 'Exit'. Quickly, he opened the trapdoor and jumped in. He sat down by his video game again!

112. Harry Enjoys Circus

Harry loved the world of animals and colourful clowns in a circus. He never missed any opportunity to visit the circus in his town. His parents took him to the new circus in town. Harry was enjoying the circus. A short man with a red nose and a pointed hat entered the ring. He scratched his yellow hair and started jumping up and down. Soon, another little man entered and threw a water balloon at him. The clown yelped and soon they were chasing each other. Harry began laughing and clapping in delight. Suddenly, a man in a long blue coat and a flat hat entered. He cracked a whip and the clowns shuddered in fear. A few lions too entered the ring. The ringmaster cracked his whip and the lions jumped through the rings of fire! Harry watched breathlessly. Harry enjoyed the circus a lot. His parents promised to take him again, if he studied and behaved well.

113. Jennifer and Amanda

Jennifer and Amanda were the best of friends. They played together. They were intelligent but innocent. They thought everyone in the world was nice. They did not realise that some people are cunning. One day, they were playing in the garden when a young woman approached them. "Little ones, will you lend me some money? I will show you a magic trick," she said. The girls loved magic tricks, so they gave the woman whatever little money they had. They were excited that they would see magic tricks. The woman then asked the children to close their eyes and count up to 10. "One, two, three...ten," the girls counted. When they opened their eyes, the woman could not be found anywhere. "That woman has tricked us," Jennifer said. "Yes." Amanda replied sadly. The girls felt extremely foolish, so they decided to be more careful with strangers, next time.

114. David and Ricky Go Fishing

David and Ricky were best friends. They shared similar likes and dislikes. Their biggest dream was to go fishing some day. They had often watched elders fishing. They would carefully watch the way a fish got stuck in the bait. David and Ricky finally had the opportunity they were waiting for. They were going fishing on Sunday and could hardly contain their excitement. "I do not understand. What's the fuss about fishing?" asked Ethan, their friend. "Maybe you should join us," offered David. The boys piled into Uncle Gomez's car and set out for the little lake. Uncle Gomez taught them how to attach the baits and throw their lines. After twenty minutes, David felt a slight tug on his line. Soon, all of them pulled at it and out came a huge fish. As the day wore on, their basket was full of fish. The boys were very excited!

115. The Amazing Toy Plane

Bentham was a small boy. He loved to play with toys. He was so fascinated with toys that he continued playing with them for hours. When it was play time, he would open his cupboard and bring out all his toys. He played with his toys alone. He did not want to share them with anyone. He liked his cousin Ronald but would not share his toys even with him. One day, Ronald and Aunt Madeleine came to visit him. Bentham was unhappy. 'If I share my toys with Ronald, he may break them,' he thought. So, he kept all his toys back in the cupboard. Just then, Aunt Madeleine came to him and said, "Here, Bentham. I have brought this amazing toy plane for you. I hope you like it." Bentham felt very ashamed about hiding his toys. Then on, he always shared his toys with Ronald.

116. Appearances Can be Deceptive

We are deceived by labels. A bottle with a ginger ale label contains ginger ale, not lemonade. But, sometimes a labelled bottle contains something different from the label. Fred hated ginger ale but loved lemonade. If he saw a bottle with the label of ginger ale, he would be disappointed. One day, Fred's family went on a picnic. They met another family there. Fred saw that they had a big bottle labelled ginger ale. The other family offered some to his brother, James. Fred ran away so that he might not have to drink the ginger ale. He only came back when the other family had left. The bottle of ginger ale was lying empty. "Oh Fred, where were you?" said Jack, "They

gave me the most delicious lemonade to drink. It was in that bottle labelled ginger ale." Fred felt very foolish. He realised that appearances can be deceptive.

117. Justin Visits France

Justin wanted to see the world. It was his lifetime dream to visit each nation of the world. He was excited at the opportunity to visit France. When he came back from the tour, he was never tired of praising France. When Justin came back from his vacation from France, he was looking for people to converse in French. He had learnt many French words and was eager to use them. "Bonjour," he cried when he met his friend Tina in the park. Tina was irritated. She didn't reply. Justin repeated the same to others at the park, but they just called him a snob. Justin wondered why everybody ignored him. His father tried to explain, "Justin, they don't understand what you are saying. But you should not let that stop you from learning new things." Forgetting his disappointment, Justin spent his remaining summer studying more French words.

118. *Joshua Saved the Puppy*

Little Joshua was a kind-hearted boy. He loved animals. He could not see animals in trouble. Whenever he found children troubling animals, he came forward to save them. One day, little boys and girls who were Joshua's friends, were playing in the park, when a tiny puppy, with an ugly snout appeared. A foul smell emanated from the dog and soon the children were kicking and pelting stones at him. The puppy yelped in terror, but the children had no pity. Little Joshua felt sorry for the puppy and shouted at the other children for troubling him. He then took the puppy home and gave him a nice hot bath. He also fed the puppy a bowl of warm milk and biscuits. The puppy wagged its tail whenever it saw Joshua. Within a few days, the puppy looked healthy. The other children felt sorry for troubling the poor puppy.

119. *Madonna's Prickling Skin*

Madonna loved to spend time on the sea-beach. Her mother gave her a sun-tan lotion to protect her skin from sunburn. She told Madonna, "Remember to use the lotion properly, Madonna. Otherwise, you will get sunburns." Madonna was excited at the prospect of going to spend time on the beach. She imagined the warmth of the beautiful sea-beach and how she would swim in the sea. She imagined all the fun she could have on the beach. Madonna finally came to the beach, but was so excited that she forgot her mother's words. She spent a wonderful hour splashing in the sea and playing with the sand. By now, the sun was directly overhead, and it was really hot. Madonna's skin started prickling and itching. She was starting to get sunburns! She immediately applied the lotion. She never forgot to use the sun-tan lotion again!

120. God's Blessings

Ethan was very sad. He wanted to enjoy with his friends. All his friends had gone to Disneyland but his parents had sent him to Aunt Eleanor's farm. He thought he would get bored at the farm. Ethan stayed in his room all day and did not talk to anyone. He was almost crying for having missed the fun at Disneyland with friends. Then, one morning, Aunt Eleanor forced him to take a walk with her. As they walked, suddenly, Ethan pointed towards a flower and said, "Oh Aunt, see, what a beautiful flower!" His aunt said, "Yes, it is the Morning Glory. My mother always said that if you see a Morning Glory, it means God sends His special blessings for you." Ethan exclaimed, "Oh! I am so sorry I was sad all this while, when God is sending me His blessings." Thereafter, Ethan enjoyed staying at the farm.

121. Martha Loves Flowers

Martha was fascinated with flowers. She especially loved beautiful flowers. While roaming in a garden she would be moved by flowers in their full blossom. She would not want to go away from the garden. She loved to pluck colourful flowers. From yellow buttercups to white daisies, she always looked carefully before choosing the flower. One day, she was playing in the garden when she saw a red rose. It was so beautiful that she felt like plucking it. Just as Martha was about to pluck it, she drew back. 'What a lovely rose! But if I pluck it, others will not be able to see the beauty of the rose,' she thought. As she ran indoors leaving the rose behind, she saw the old lady next door smiling at the beautiful rose. Martha felt glad she had not plucked the red rose. It could now give enjoyment to others.

122. Jimmy Will not Lie Again

Jimmy was a good boy, but he had some bad habits. He was lazy and he lied. His parents told him many times to give up bad habits but he did not listen to them. "Jimmy!" yelled his mother, "You promised to help father mow the lawn." Jimmy was too lazy to work in the garden. Jimmy wondered, "How do I get out of this?" He decided to lie, and said, "Mother, I have a test tomorrow, so I need to study." Jimmy then hid a comic in his text-book and started reading. In the evening, he got dressed to visit the park. However, he realised that his father was not yet dressed. "Aren't we going to the park?" asked Jimmy. "No, I have some paper work," said father. "You promised me," wailed Jimmy. "So did you," said his father, smiling. Jimmy was ashamed. He never lied again.

123. Adventurous Trip

Ritzier and Joseph were good friends but their nature was not alike. In fact, their nature was quite opposite. If Ritzier was happy-go-lucky, Joseph was cautious. So, they thought and behaved in opposite ways. They were on a family hiking trip in Canada when both boys went out for a walk. Ritzier wanted to see the sunset from the mountain top. "Joseph, let's climb to the top of the mountain," he said. Joseph was afraid of the climb and said, "But Ritzier, what if we fall?" Ritzier smiled and said, "Joseph, if we climb carefully, we will not fall. If you want to see the view from the top, you have to climb the mountain." Joseph was initially not interested but became motivated after Ritzier had convinced him. Finally, Joseph agreed to go with Ritzier. Both boys saw the beautiful view from the top. Joseph realised that making an effort has rewards.

124. Grandpa Murphy

Grandpa Murphy was a grumpy old man. He hated children because he thought that children are mischievous. The children too disliked him. They avoided him because he was always yelling and chasing them around with his stout brown stick. One day, Allen entered Grandpa's garden to smell the pink peonies and deep red roses. When Grandpa saw him, he shouted and ran after him. Allen was scared. He ran away to save his life. At home, Allen told his mother about the incident. His mother smiled. She thought of a scheme to please the Grandpa. She asked Allen to take some flower pots to Grandpa the next time. The next day, Allen gifted Grandpa two flower pots. "My mother says this will make you happy," said Allen. Grandpa could not help but smile. Soon, Allen was a regular visitor. They became the best of friends. Grandpa began to like children.

125. Susan Has Friends

The Wilkinson family had two daughters and four sons. On Sundays, they would pile into a white wagon and go to the park, or museum, or to the lakeside. That would be a huge affair from morning to evening. Children are social by nature. They love to play with other children. They do not want to be alone. Wilkinson family's children formed a big group. However, some children like Susan were not so lucky. Little Susan, an only child, was Wilkinson's neighbour. She would often see the Wilkinson family laughing and playing together, and wished that she too had someone to play with. One day, Susan was sitting alone in her garden, while Wilkinson children were playing with a ball. The ball rolled into Susan's garden. When she returned the ball, they invited her to play with them. Since then, Susan became friends with them. She was never lonely again!

126. *Mylie Loves Water Fountains*

Mylie had many hobbies, interests and likes, but she was fascinated with water. She loved water sports. If she had nothing to do, she could keep watching the water fountain for hours. Mylie loved to play with water alone without the company of friends. At parks, she would often stare at water fountains for long hours. She would feel good and happy while concentrating on rising and falling water. One day, Mylie went to stay at a hotel with her family on a trip to London. That evening, Mylie was walking in the hotel lobby when she heard someone say, "Isn't it time for the magic water fountain to start?" Mylie looked around and saw a magnificent water fountain. It shot out colourful streams of water from its centre while music played. Mylie realised that even different colours can make the water fountain truly magical because each shade is unique.

127. *A Castle of Sand*

Giovanni loved to swim in the blue sea and play on the sand at the beach. One afternoon, she was walking on the beach when she saw a huge crowd collected on the shoreline. She wondered why the crowd had gathered there. As she walked across, Giovanni moved closer to the crowd. She saw that a group of people had built a massive sandcastle. It was so large that the tower of the castle touched the top of a sun umbrella. 'Wow,' thought Giovanni, 'That is the biggest and strongest castle ever.' It was very tall. She looked above and wondered how tall it was. She approached the tower and touched it. She felt that the castle was very strong. Suddenly, a huge wave crashed into the sandcastle. The castle was completely destroyed. It turned into a heap of sand once again. Giovanni realised that size is no guarantee of strength!

128. *Marlene's Red Umbrella*

Marlene worked at a bookshop around the corner. She carried a red umbrella to work every day. Everyone else who worked in the shop owned a grey or black one. Marlene's umbrella stood out and looked cheerful even on the dullest days. Also, Marlene never had any trouble identifying the umbrella in a shop rack. Marlene felt proud of her red umbrella. She felt she looked beautiful and elegant with the umbrella over her head. She walked with confidence and style whenever the umbrella stood sideways over her head. She felt like a princess. One day, Marlene picked the red umbrella up and stepped out. Suddenly, she felt water trickling down her back. She saw that her umbrella had a leak! She was quite upset at first, but then her mother bought a bright yellow umbrella for her and said, "Marlene, change can be a good thing. Adopt change."

129. *Charles Loves His Colourful Book*

Charles was a nursery student. He loved his nursery book. His nursery book was extremely colourful and contained wonderful illustrations and stories. He would keep turning one colourful page after the other. Charles's babysitter Vanessa always narrated the stories to him. Charles loved reading along with her, tracing out the pictures. He would ask her questions, while she answered each of his questions. One day, Charles's Aunt Jennifer came to visit him. She gifted him with a new nursery book. It had many more pictures. It also contained a lot of new stories. The old nursery book did not look so appealing to Charles anymore, so he put it away. After many days, Charles took out the old book again. Charles realised that he still loved the old stories, even though he had read so many new ones. He remembered the old stories. He thought all stories were good.

130. The Snowman Who Helps

Azarias was a young boy. He loved fun and frolic. He would run around here and there. His parents often warned him, "Azarias, be careful while crossing the road. Look at both the sides before crossing." Once, Azarias was badly hurt in an accident. The doctors warned his parents, "He won't be able to walk ever again." Azarias was heart-broken and lay in bed all day, angry and upset. One night, it was snowing heavily. Azarias looked out from his window when he saw a massive snowman walking in the middle of the garden. He could not believe his eyes! As he watched, the snowman stopped at his window and said, "Azarias, you can walk again. Go on; try." Excited, Azarias stood up and started walking. As he turned to thank the snowman, he saw it dashed through clouds and flew to the skies. Azarias thanked God for the miracle.

131. Hale and His Granny

Hale loved to watch TV. He would be irritated when he could not see his favourite cartoon show. Once, there was no electricity in his house. Hale was crying because he

could not watch TV. He kept on pestering his granny. It was a cold, dark morning without electricity while Hale was wailing aloud. Hale complained to his granny, "I can't live without electricity or TV! You know that very well. Why don't you do something?" "Okay; let's light the magic lamp," said granny. She took out an old lamp and poured some oil into it. She lit the lamp. The room became brighter. Hale looked on in awe at the shadows formed by the flame on the wall. Granny said, "See; electricity isn't that important. A small lamp can also magically light up the entire room. We must enjoy the moment we live in and look for magic in it."

132. Kaddish, the Dragon

Kaddish felt very lonely. He was a fire-breathing dragon, so everyone would run away from him in alarm. Although Kaddish was a fire-breathing dragon yet he did not want to hurt anyone. He was a nice dragon. He was disappointed that no one came near to him. All the fairies, imps, goblins, gnomes and the people would pass him by. None of them even looked at him. So, he stopped calling them. One day, Marshall, a young boy, was visiting the neighbouring village across the forest. He saw Kaddish sitting all alone and approached him. "Go away!" said Kaddish in alarm, "I am a fire-breathing dragon, so you may get hurt." "I doubt that. You see; I am immune to fire," said Marshall. Kaddish realised that differences are what make people special and true friends are not hard to find even if you breathe out fire!

133. Lucille's Bad Wishes

Lucille was a naughty girl who troubled everyone. She loved wishing trouble on others. Her parents had warned her not to trouble others. Her class teacher was fed up with her. Her class friends always complained about her. But Lucille did not change. 'Oh, I do wish Ms. Mary would fall down from the chair,' she would think, or 'I wish Samson would step into that dirty puddle.' One day, Lucille was walking to school when she saw a massive truck of garbage on the road. 'How funny it would be if the garbage fell on the old dog that likes to bark at me! I wish it would happen!' thought Lucille. Just then, the truck veered and garbage fell on her as well as the dog! From then on, Lucille wished for only good things. 'I should think good of others. Goodness brings happiness to everyone,' she thought.

134. Jenna Wants to Cook

Jenna loved to cook. She had learnt to cook a number of dishes. She delighted in cooking and loved to share with others the delicacies she prepared. She especially loved baking cookies and pizzas at home. One day, she visited her Aunt Nadia. Her aunt had also prepared pizza for the night. Jenna loved it. Jenna wondered why she did not make so delicious pizzas while Aunt Nadia could make awesome pizzas. When she asked her aunt how it was made, she was surprised to know that it was no different from how she cooked it. "But why is your pizza so delicious?" asked Jenna. Her aunt smiled and took her to the garden. "I grow my own vegetables, which I use for cooking. It's not only about how you cook the pizza, but what you put into it also matters," said her aunt. Jenna never forgot this important lesson!

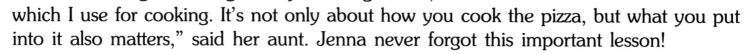

135. Beckett and the Little Imp

Beckett was a nice girl. She lived in her own world of thoughts. She had many dolls and toys, she loved to play with. Now she longed for a pet. She imagined the fun she would have playing with her pet. She thought life would be wonderful in the company of a pet. One day, she was sitting in the garden when she saw a small imp. "Hello, would you like to be my pet?" asked Beckett. "I would love it," said the imp. So, Beckett happily took the imp home. But the imp was restless as the evening grew. "What is it?" asked Beckett as the imp became fidgety. "I want to go and play," said the imp. "But it is tea time," said Beckett. The imp refused to listen and ran out. Beckett realised that bringing a pet home was easier than keeping it there!

136. Manfred, the Good Goblin

All goblins are not bad. Some goblins are good. Manfred was a nice goblin. Manfred wanted to make friends with everyone. But no one wanted to be friends with a goblin. The fairies were especially scared of goblins. So, they avoided Manfred. One day, Manfred went to meet the fairies and the imps. Jenna, the good fairy, saw him and said, "Look at the ugly goblin!" "I would never be a goblin's friend!" Felix, the imp, laughed. Manfred felt very bad. He was extremely disappointed at the behaviour of the fairies and the imps. He didn't know what to do. As he turned to return home, he heard someone shouting, "Jeffrey, the queen fairy's son, is stuck in the swamp." Manfred went to the swamp, threw a long stick to Jeffrey and pulled him with all his might. Soon, Jeffrey was out of the swamp. All the fairies thanked Manfred and became his friends.

137. Craig's Toy Car

Craig was fascinated with new toys. He loved toy cars. He would never tire of playing with the toy cars. Craig would ask his parents to buy new toys every now and then. One day, Craig saw a shiny toy car in the shop window. The shiny toy car fascinated him. He thought he would buy the car even if it was expensive. He collected all his pocket money. 'What a wonderful way to spend my pocket money!' thought Craig. He was about to buy the toy car when he remembered he had promised to give the money to an orphanage. This was his good deed for the day. Reluctantly, he walked away. When he reached home, his mother told him that Aunt Sylvia from London had sent him a gift. Craig tore open the gift-wrapping to see the same toy car! He said in joy, "Mom, see how I am rewarded for my kindness."

138. James Saw the Golden Fairy

James believed in only what he saw. He had never seen anything magical. So, he never believed in magic. He would make fun of other children who believed in magic. He said that those who believed in fairies, dwarfs and imps were fools. One night, as his mother tucked him in and left the room, James saw a shiny light outside the window. To his surprise, it was a little fairy flapping her golden wings! James ran to the window, but the fairy smiled and vanished before he could reach. James wondered in surprise. As the days passed, James often looked out of the window. But not finding anything, he forgot about the golden fairy. One night, the fairy returned. "Who are you? Why are you here?" asked James curiously. She smiled and said, "I came to show you that magic exists." James started believing in magic from that day on.

139. Life's Surprises

Matthew loved his granny. She would tell him stories every day. He was waiting for his granny's birthday. Actually, he wanted to surprise his granny. He had planned a surprise party for his granny. She was turning 80 this year. 'What a wonderful party it will be!' thought Matthew, as he planned everything. He wanted this party something

that his granny would remember forever. But on that day, a hurricane swept through town. It spoiled his arrangements. Matthew felt very sad. All his grand plans had completely failed. Just then, his granny came in and showed him a beautiful picture. "Look Matthew; see how beautiful I looked when I was young. Frankly, 80 is not an age I want to celebrate. I want to forget it, not remember it," she said wistfully. Matthew smiled and thought that even life's little surprises have a way of working out for the best.

140. *Mark Helps the Gnome*

Mark was a nice boy. He helped everyone in need. He was especially helpful to those who were in distress. If someone called out for help, Mark volunteered as fast as he could. One day, Mark's class went on a field trip. In a cave, he saw a green gnome tied to a rock. Mark was moved by his condition. Just as the gnome saw Mark, he shouted, "Please help me. My name is Duncan. An evil giant trapped me here. He will eat me when he gets back." Reassuring Duncan, Mark quickly untied him. Then, they both ran off to save themselves. That evening, as Mark and his class were returning home, their bus got stuck on a cliff. The bus was about to fall off, when suddenly, Duncan appeared and pushed their bus back on to the road. Mark was happy that his kindness had been rewarded.

141. *Miranda Loves Her Mom*

All children love their mothers. While mothers do everything for their children throughout the year, the Mother's Day is the only occasion when children can do something

for their mothers. Miranda loved her mother. She thought her mother was the best Mom in the world. As Mother's Day was coming closer, Miranda wondered what she could get for her Mom. She finally bought a beautiful crystal from a shop with her pocket money. On Mother's day, as Miranda was picking the gift up, it fell and smashed on the floor. Miranda began to cry and her Mom came running to her. When she explained why she was crying, her Mom smiled and said, "Don't cry, Miranda. The most precious gift I can ever have is you." Miranda felt happy. Miranda realised that day that the best and most precious gifts are not those that we can buy from a shop.

142. George and His Grandpa

George loved his Grandpa. They would often go together to the park or cafe. Grandpa would tell George interesting stories. They would sit together in the cafe and relish their coffee. George would ask him too many questions, but Grandpa never got bored in his company. He answered all his questions. Grandpa loved to sit on the tall chair in the cafe, while George would wander about and choose a small one. 'Oh, how nice it would be to sit on the tall chair!' George would think longingly. One day, Grandpa was buying a lamp from the furniture shop and George was also there. There was a small chair on display in the window shop. "Look at that small chair. I wish I could fit into it. It would be so much fun," remarked Grandpa wistfully. George smiled as he realised that the grass always seems greener on the other side.

143. Jennifer and Her Grandpa

Jennifer was a little girl with boundless curiosity. She loved to read books. She had too many questions, the answers to which could be found in those books. She loved to visit libraries to read books. She felt bored with life, if she did not find anything to read. In her Grandpa's library, there was a big, green book which she was not allowed to read. She would always wonder what was in that book. One afternoon, it was raining and Jennifer felt curious to know more about the big, green book. It was on a high shelf. As she pulled it, it fell and bruised her arm. She opened it excitedly. She was amazed to see that the pages of the book were in tatters and not a word could be read. Not only had she hurt herself, but also wasted her time. Jennifer realised the value of obeying her Grandpa.

144. Jenna and Her Planes

Jenna was creative in nature. She wanted to learn new things. She had learnt to make paper planes. She would now keep making paper planes. She never got tired of making paper planes. She wanted to make a perfect paper plane that glided and landed smoothly. She would often release paper planes into the breeze. She specially loved making such planes from coloured paper. One day, as she was making yet another plane, she saw the boy next door making a beautiful wooden boat using tools. Jenna watched in fascination as the new boat was made. It was raining and the boy excitedly set the boat on a puddle. It sank and Jenna realised just because the boat looked beautiful did not mean it would be perfect in every way. She taught the boy to make paper boats and both of them enjoyed watching them float on the water.

145. Susan and Bruno

Susan was a small girl. She was only six years old but she was quite intelligent. She loved to play with pets. Once, her mother got her a clever dog. The name of the dog was Bruno. Susan loved her clever dog, Bruno. Her mother trusted Bruno because he

always took care of Susan. One day, when Susan was playing with her dolls, she realised that Bruno was missing. She saw that the back door was open. So, she sneaked out to look for Bruno. When Susan was walking down the lane, she felt someone pulling at her dress. It was Bruno! "Oh, where were you? You naughty dog!" said Susan. But Bruno kept pulling her till they reached home. Meanwhile, Susan's mother was looking everywhere for her. She scolded Susan for going out alone. Susan told her everything, and promised not to go out alone. Her mother thanked Bruno.

146. Stephen's Purple Boat

Stephen loved to make paper boats. He imagined going on long voyages on his boat. He imagined encountering dangers along the way but also imagined successfully fighting against the dangers. One day, Stephen made a huge purple paper boat and kept it on his bedside table. At midnight, a loud noise woke him up. To his surprise, Stephen saw a captain and some sailors on his boat! "Why don't you come aboard, my boy?" asked the captain. Stephen was excited. He saw his dream coming true. "Sure," said Stephen as he set off across the water, which filled his room, out of his house and into the street. There, they met a pirate ship. "Let's give them a good fight," shouted the captain and together they defeated the pirates. Then, the purple paper boat dropped Stephen off on his bed. No one knew the adventures he had been on!

147. Parker and Yellow Paintbrush

Parker loved to paint and draw. Painting was his sole passion. He would be found painting day and night. He would keep experimenting with different paint brushes. But

he had no patience. If a paint brush didn't work, he threw it away. One day, he found an old paintbrush in the school art room. Thinking he would have fun with it, he dipped it in water. To his amazement, the water turned yellow. He thought it was a lovely brush. He wondered if it could change colours, so he tried dipping it again. But the colour remained yellow. Parker tossed the paintbrush aside. 'What is the use of a paintbrush that has only one colour?' he thought. Just then, the teacher announced that they would be drawing and colouring bananas that day. Parker now realised how useful the paintbrush was. He should not have been so hasty to throw it away.

148. Honey, the Talking Bunny

Maria was not interested in studies. All she wanted was to have fun and play. She played truant and did not listen to her parents or her teachers. Maria was always playing when it was time to study. On the top of it, if her mother warned her, she made faces. One day, she played truant from her study lessons at home and ran to the garden. She saw a small bunny sitting on the swing. "Hello, I'm Honey. Isn't it time to study right now?" asked the little bunny. Maria was surprised. "How can you talk?" she asked Honey, surprised. "I learnt to talk from my teacher. But you should go back and study. Then later, when it is time to play, we can play together," replied Honey. Maria ran back to the study. She was careful and studied and played at the right time from then on.

149. Sampson and Matthew

Sampson and Matthew were good friends. Sampson admired Matthew because he thought Matthew was smart and bold. Sampson also feared Matthew because he was unpredictable. Sampson admired his friend Matthew a lot but Matthew did not give Sampson any importance. Matthew was very smart and he knew how to add big numbers, unlike any other boy in the class. So Sampson often kept quiet whenever Matthew spoke. One afternoon, as both the boys were walking back from school, Matthew saw a huge puddle. As Matthew stopped there, Sampson became suspicious. "If I jump gently in the centre of the puddle, dirty water will not splash on me," said Matthew. Before Sampson could stop him, Matthew jumped into the puddle. As it turned out, the puddle was deep and even a soft splash covered Matthew in dirt. Sampson realised that being smart also means being careful. After all, we cannot know everything.

150. Dracula, the Wolf

Dracula was a very naughty wolf. Children were scared of him. Dracula delighted in scaring children. Whenever children didn't behave well, their moms would often tell them to behave well or Dracula would come. Although all children were scared of Dracula yet the little boy Matt was especially scared of him. He lived in the cottage by the forest. Dracula loved to scare poor Matt. He didn't want to harm Matt but simply used to scare him. Dracula would howl in the night and scare Matt a lot. One night, when there was a full moon, Dracula decided it was time to frighten Matt again. Just as he started howling, he heard a hunter coming into the forest. In his panic, Dracula ran into a trap and started whining. Hearing this, Matt came out with his father and released Dracula from the trap. Dracula stopped teasing Matt or anyone else.

151. Jonas Plays Prank

Jonas was a naughty child. He never sat down to study but always wanted to have fun. Jonas loved to play pranks on others. His mother used to admonish him but Jonas never listened to anyone. He loved to play pranks so much that he did not care about the consequences of his pranks. One morning, Jonas's mother made his favourite pancakes for school lunch. Just as the class was beginning that day, Jonas placed a mechanical rubber spider on the floor. He wound it up and it moved across the floor. There were loud shouts as all the girls and the boys ran away from the spider. Jonas was about to laugh when he saw that the spider had charged onto the cabinet and dislodged the lunch boxes there. His pancakes were on the floor! Jonas realised how even harmless pranks could turn out to be not so funny after all!